The Changing Moors

Uniform with this volume

THE CHANGING DALES
CHANGING LAKELAND

The Changing Moors

Forty Years of "Progress" in North-East Yorkshire

by
John Tindale

Preface by Eric Halsall

Dalesman Books
1990

THE DALESMAN PUBLISHING COMPANY LTD.,
CLAPHAM, via Lancaster, LA2 8EB

First published 1990

ISBN: 0 85206 996 0

To Ruth Kitching
Friend and Mentor

Printed by Peter Fretwell & Sons Ltd., Keighley, West Yorkshire BD21 1PZ

CONTENTS

PHOTOGRAPHS

All uncredited photographs by the author

Opposite: America Jack (see pages 27-34). He dealt with a kicking pony at Hinderwell Show by lifting a foreleg off the ground. "If it kicks now it'll fall over," he said.

EPILOGUE BY A MODERN FARMER

PREFACE

THE story is twofold. Today, now, it is an enjoyable read of country ways on the North York Moors, and the pictures are first class in illustrating these ways. Tomorrow, in the future, it may well be a piece of agricultural history.

John Tindale has that happy knack of writing in a conversational way so that *The Changing Moors* becomes a personal chat with the reader on a way of life. If the Politicians have too much say and 1992 turns out to be not the Eldorado it is painted, this account of that way of life on the North York Moors will become a document of great significance to the agricultural historian.

The book records the farming scene in the area from the start of the 20th century, through the war years, to the present time. Farming is unmatched as an industry so deeply rooted in the past and yet so characterised by change which has had far-reaching consequences on the development of society as a whole, and the farming of the old North Riding has played its part. The book reminiscences with farmers of yesteryear and looks forward with farmers of today, and consequently the reader gets a true picture of the area.

John Tindale's story is bang up-to-date, and one reads with a grin spreading to a chuckle of the crafts of characters who made the farming of the Yorkshire moors so interesting and productive, and so personal. Sheepdogs have brought me to know the area. I have judged trials in North Yorkshire. I think of the characters I have met, and deplore this passing, yet they will never die whilst this story is around.

Often when discussing the content of the *One Man and his Dog* programmes at the Television Centre in London we raise the question of country characters and crafts, for as the viewers will know, the "magazine items" are as popular almost as the skills of the dogs. This book is full of such characters and their crafts, and there is never a dull moment in reading of their exploits.

Eric Halsall
Cliviger, 1990

INTRODUCTION

We plough the fields and scatter
The good seed on the land
And it is fed and watered
By God's almighty hand.

The winds and waves obey Him
But not the E.E.C.
Who deal in lakes and mountains
And grow crops by decree.

1992 — The Year of Destiny looms when all Europe shall be one, when the French will greet with smiling faces imports from the U.K., when all shall be harmony and light. Some of the small Continental farms would seem to have more in common with British farming of 1892 with their productivity needing all the Green Pounds it can get, whilst the North Yorkshire hill men have inherent problems caused more by the landscape. This book reminiscences with some North Yorkshire characters and tries to look forward through the comments of modern men who were asked where farming was going in the next ten years.

The North York Moors National Park Executive gave his opinion that changes are likely to be fundamental and far reaching: "It is possible that many of our farmers will disappear because of the over-production of food. The farming landscape we have inherited is outdated so far as its primary function of producing food is concerned, but may have claims for public support because of its environmental, cultural and social values." That is certainly not the opinion of Mr Martin Burrt, a working farmer who is involved in the NFU on both a local and national basis and whose nightmare would be the handing over of farming interests from the Ministry of Agriculture to the Department of the Environment — his full comments appear in a later chapter.

The decline in the number of farms seems to be borne out by farming friends who are, or are considering, selling up and who, presumably, will be cheered on in that direction by the 1988 Budget which virtually eliminated Capital gains Tax on values accruing in the crazy inflation period up to 1982.

From man's beginning there must have been cultivation for food — Adam and Eve presumably didn't live entirely on apples — and since we are told that man first existed in Africa (as a white Adam and Eve?) the climate presumably was much different from these northern moors. The Romans were here and left their mark with the Roman road from Hunt House, Goathland, and in the names of several farms, and certainly they cultivated the land to feed their legions. In 1988 the archaeologists decided that the major fort near Newcastle then being excavated had been used as grain storage for their troops doing battle with the Scots. The monks at Whitby must either have farmed or made the locals work for them; they certainly were major landowners, as were and are the various lords of the manors. Even those who today own their own farms must feel that the government and the National Park authorities tend to act as absentee landlords demanding their tithe!

Sometime before 5000 BC a revolution took place in the Middle East which eventually spread all over Europe. This was the introduction of farming; before that a single family had needed many miles of land to roam in search of game, but for sowing crops and raising livestock a few acres were enough. It was around 4000 BC before the revolution reached the British Isles; that it did so was due to farmers across the Channel in Brittany being under threat from marauding tribes, and deciding to migrate northwards. The locals, being hunters, did battle with them, but eventually came to admit the benefits of the new system and the fashion for farming instead of hunting spread.

The newcomers also brought new ideas in housing — the trees they felled to clear the land for crops were used for house building, and cleared areas were surrounded with wattle pallisades. The children were used to guard the flock of brown fleeced sheep and to watch that cattle did not wander on to the growing corn. These animals were brought inside the pallisade at night to protect them from marauding wolves.

Perhaps it is enough to go back to the beginning of this 20th century or just before, for in the ensuing period there have been a multitude of changes. While it is true that here in the north we have not seen a major elimination of hedges to form prairies for multi-ploughed tractors, nor the use by shepherds of motor cycles with skis fitted for shepherding on high hills, as in some areas of Scotland, many things have indeed changed.

Changed for the better? Sometimes yes, but, as the late Tom Morley of Brock Hall Farm said to me: "I've just written a cheque for £3,500 for artificial fertiliser and we're still spreading the same amount of muck — I don't know why." The fact that the Ministry's latest paperwork suggests a programme of organic farming to cut back on yields would seem to give the answer and maybe an indication as to why there are food mountains. Who would have thought that increased production would become over-production, grain mountains a blot on the Common Market and the media would be telling stories of hard-headed farmers turning their fields into leisure centres, farm holiday centres, organic food and nature conservancy parks with horse ploughing an advertised attraction.

The field of waving corn has had to be chopped back a couple of metres around the edges: the hedgerows which were removed to make way for prairie tractors are to be replaced in the name of conservation, the open vistas clothed in trees for profit in fifty years time. The patter of the chemical fertiliser salesmen must no longer bring dreams of avarice and more and more grass — and surely with the electronic revolution it will soon be possible to programme the cows to produce exactly the volume of milk the Common Agricultural Policy decrees? Probably only fair because the bulls had their natural instincts frozen many years ago.

A return to nature for the farming fraternity?

JOHN TINDALE RECALLS

WHAT right has a town dweller to write about farming matters? The fact is that for some thirty years I travelled around the North Yorkshire area — when it was the North Riding — taking photographs and writing stories about characters I met, and that I used a tape recorder to make sure I was not taken to task for misquoting them. Most importantly, I was very involved with the late and much lamented America Jack (John Welford of America House Farm), and the Cleveland Bay Horse Society under the auspices of Miss Ruth Kitching, which was an education to be treasured and unlikely to be repeated.

But in a small town like Whitby there is not a clear line between town and country — except, it must be said, in the opinions of the old Rural District Councillors and those who have succeeded them on the Borough Council. Their attitudes are those of their neighbours and electors, some of whom still regard town dwellers as unnecessary nuisances who traipse over fields with unruly dogs, and who cherish a particular dislike for those with delusions about footpaths and "rights of way".

My connections with farming are also historic for my ancestors on the distaff side were Stevensons, originally from Pickering. John Stevenson, my great-uncle, had an association with farming because he was a chemist and veterinary surgeon in Baxtergate, Whitby, up to around 1890 in the days when vets were not registered. He, and Reg Maw at Ruswarp who continued until the late 1930s, were a thorn in the flesh of the "qualified" vets because their nostrums were preferred by the farming community! Matthew Stevenson farmed at High Light, near Saltwick Bay, until the late 1940s and would be one of the last to thatch his stacks, one with a fox and the other with a chicken. His housekeeper, Mrs Pickering, used to deliver eggs and butter to us on Saturdays up to the 1940s and exchange them for the baking powder my pharmacist-father used to manufacture — packed in cartons fastened with a blob of red sealing wax.

I also have memories back to the 1920s when milk didn't come in bottles. The milkman arrived at the back door with his can, probably holding a couple of gallons, and with pint and half-pint measures hooked on the rim. His name was Henry Thistle who farmed at Abbeylands Farm beside the Abbey. He was necessarily a very early riser for he had milked his cows, cooled the output, harnessed his horse into the trap, loaded a couple of churns and set off on the mile or so to our house on the other side of town, delivering to other houses on his way and still arriving with us around 8.30 a.m., before I set off for school. He must have spent time changing his clothes for he was always smartly dressed in a jacket, knee-length breeches and long socks; my memory says it was a dark whipcord outfit and that the horse in the shafts was much the same colour. It must have been during school holidays when I was six or seven years old that heaven was a ride further up the road on the back step of the trap.

Mother — or the maid, for we had one in those days who was usually a teenager from a farming family — met him at the back door with a two-pint earthenware basin. I seem to remember a bluish tinge on top of the milk; I don't remember cream but that was probably because the milk was well mixed by its journeyings. Whatever the quantity wanted there was always an extra dip in his can to make up for any shortfall, described as "a drop for the cat". We never had a cat, but our Sealyham terrier would appreciate a drop — as much as he would have enjoyed nipping an ankle if allowed out!

We had no refrigerator and there was no ice, yet the milk seemed to keep without trouble on the stone floor of the pantry with some being decanted into a jug as required. This was covered with a lacy bit of material which had beads, blue ones I think, around its edges to counterweight it. Mr Thistle's cooling would be with water from an unusual source; his farm and another nearby had the same supply as the Abbey and it came in wood conduits from near Hawsker where there was, and still is St. Hilda's Well. In the farmyard there still is a water tower.

Lest anyone think we were a particularly affluent family, the fact that we had a live-in maid from an outlying village was not unusual because, whilst social attitudes have changed, the attitudes of teenagers, basically, have not. Whilst our young lady had not the benefits of Social Security to help with her desire to flee the family nest, a few years living in the nearest town in a house with "mod cons" and doing housework not much different to what she would have been expected to do at home, a bedroom of her own, plus a visit to the Empire Cinema and a boy friend allowed in the kitchen during the evening, plus pocket money, made being a maid an attractive proposition — and in any case there was then no particular social stigma attached to the title, at least in our house.

Move on a few years, to the days of the innocent yearnings of an eleven-year-old boy at a local, mixed, school where there were the three daughters of a farm on the edge of town, one of whom, a year older than I, was the subject of my adoration from afar. Which is why I engineered myself into being a slave labourer shovelling out from the cow shed into the midden, loading same into a horse-drawn cart and manually spreading it on the fields. Or preferably, and the height of rapture, carrying buckets of steaming milk from the cowshed — manual milking of course — to the dairy where "she" officiated, in the hope that she would consent to go for a walk, or even better go to the pictures with me. All to no avail for she finally, and probably in desperation said, "Why don't you ask my sister, she's more your age." In fact, she was one year younger! Neither was she interested in my cow-eyed advances.

The countryside always had its attraction for town-bred children and not always for nature study reasons; the days of potato-picking school holidays seem to have mostly died out but certainly in the early days of this century they were more than a source of pocket money, particularly to the children of the fishing community. Fishermen, like farmers, have always had the reputation for bemoaning their financial impecuniousness and I would not presume to question that, but, listening to the late "Woodpeg" Storry, of a Whitby fishing family whose mother had died in 1895 when he was two and whose father was frequently unable to go to sea in his small coble because of bad weather in the days of no unemployment benefit and no other income, the chance of picking potatoes or turnips was a necessity for the boy; the prospects depended on the farmer, but two shillings a day was "about right". Woodpeg smacked his lips as he recalled working for Richardson's at Cross Butts Farm where, whilst they only paid one and sixpence (7p) a day, there was a good rabbit pie dinner. "There would be about nine of us round the table, starving, and she opened the door and came in with the pie. We all sat there with mouths drooling and rubbing our hands." The moment when the pie was cut and the plates filled was a vision that was still in Woodpeg's memory seventy years later.

Officially working for a farmer was one thing; expeditions by town boys into the countryside at times had other purposes, like brambling, and it was on such an outing that Alderman James

Danby Dale: just visible on the skyline are the masts of the RAF Station at Danby Beacon, an important communications centre in the 2nd World War.

Roadside view of the cruck barn at Ainthorpe, which was later renovated and thatched, 1969.

Fletcher recalled that he and another lad stopped half way up Skelder near a turnip field — and took a turnip. He went on, "I've often thought to myself that was stealing and I've tried to ease my conscience by saying that when the Day of Judgement comes the Almighty will say it was feeding the hungry and we'll let it go at that. At least I hope he will . . . the fact that we later found some crab apples and ate them was possibly punishment enough."

One wartime memory of mine is of pulling our truck into the roadside for a brew-up somewhere in Belgium near a farmhouse; we had hardly stopped when the farmer came out and, in urgent rapid French which we did not understand, and arm waving which we took to be an appeal for assistance, ushered three of us into an outhouse where a cow was laid on her side moaning. He slowed down his speech enough for me to remember some words of schoolboy French and his problem was that he needed strong arms to pull gently on a rope attached to the front legs of a calf in process of being born. This was accomplished, the calf was a female and he was delighted — so much so that our normal brew-up of dried milk, tea leaves and sugar in a can suspended over a petrol stove was exchanged for a proper cupper, plus a dozen fresh eggs and enough milk for the rest of the day.

The Court Leet, protector of common land and ancient rights, meets in the only main room remaining at Danby Castle with (right) Viscount Downe, a major landowner in the area. Danby Castle is reputed to have been the place where Henry VIII's Jane Seymour awaited her escorts to take her to her marriage.

Above: Hunting attracts objectors nowadays and landowners ban hunts from their fields, but one hunting expedition has had repercussions for 900 years. The Planting of the Penny Hedge in the upper harbour at Whitby dates back to the reign of King Henry II when some noblemen went hunting wild boar. "The hounds ran him very well near about the Chapel and Hermitage of Eskdaleside and the boar, sore wounded and hot pursued, took in at the Chapel door." The hermit monk shut the door, the noblemen were annoyed and broke in "and did most violently run at the hermit with their boar staves, whereof he died".

Before he died he forgave them provided that on the eve of Ascension Day they planted a hedge of "ten stakes, ten Stout-Strowers and ten Yedders to be cut with a knife of penny price" on the harbourside at Whitby and if it did not withstand three tides their lands should be forfeit. The Allansons and Huttons, as tenants of the land, carried out the penance faithfully until around 1985 when, because it was a high tide, the hedge could not be planted. This expunged the penance, but the ceremony still carries on as a tourist attraction.

Opposite, top: The Queen Mother with Lord Normanby on Lythe green; other royal visitors have included King Olav of Norway, Princess Margaret and the Duchess of Kent.

Opposite, bottom: An open air mass is held each year, alternately at Egton Bridge and Ugthorpe, to the memory of Father Nicholas Postgate, martyred at York for his priesthood and his name is now being promoted for beatification.

George and Isaac Scarth making besoms at Rock Head Cottage, Glaisdale, near Whitby — a photograph taken by Frank Meadow Sutcliffe about the turn of the last century. (Copyright: Sutcliffe Gallery, Whitby).

The Vicar of Sleights, near Whitby, was among those prosecuted in 1906 for participating in cock fighting — two hundred years after it was ruled to be illegal. This complete pit stands near Woodlands, Sleights, on private property — and was more recently used as a sunny retreat for sisters of a religious order!

Traditionally the first Monday in January is Plough Monday, and the previous day the Goathland Plough Stots carry a wood plough through the village to the church. The Plough Stot sword dancing tradition dates back, it is said, to Viking times. Certainly some of the farms in the area have Viking or Roman names.

Quoits, a traditional sport in the Esk Valley, involves throwing a 5 1/4 lbs metal ring over a pitch of eleven yards to try and drop over the pin. This match was at Robin Hood's Bay.

Above: Dry stone walling at the top of Skelder, above Whitby.

Left: Renovation of the machinery at Ugthorpe Mill in 1956 included fitting a cog wheel with cherry wood teeth. Re-toothed by Bernard Knaggs of Low Hawsker, its purpose was to cut down the noise by eliminating a similar metal-toothed cog wheel, and was a common feature of mills.

Dora Palmer, who travelled the district singing "Vessel Cups", (presumably Wassail Cups), starting in October and completing her rounds by Christmas. She carried a small box containing a doll as an effigy of the Christ child, sang her verses and then waited for a cash contribution. It was the common feeling that failure to pay up would bring on the "Evil Eye".

AMERICA JACK

IF there is one denizen of the North Yorks. Moors who belongs in this book it must be the late John Welford of America House Farm, Hinderwell — an unfamiliar name for a well-beloved man better known as America Jack. I make no apologies to those who have read an earlier book of mine about him for repeating some of the material. Good tales are worth telling twice or even more . . .

America House Farm is on the edge of the moor above Hinderwell, on the Whitby-Loftus road, the long low buildings with their backs to the North Sea. The Welford family have been there from the days when it was known as "Spring Farm" in the early 1800s; they were tenants of the Turton family as they are to this day. in 1854 we know that William Welford was there, followed by Thomas — who objected to a proposed improvement in drainage, which presumably would have put up the rent, and left the farm. The Harding family took over, paid no rent and were evicted in 1885 by which time they had chopped up the stairs and window frames and the beams from the cow shed for firewood. They were supposed to have come from America and it was they who changed the name to "America House".

In 1887 the Turtons asked George, son of Thomas, to go back. The farm had been empty for two years, wild rabbits were in the house, fences gone and much of the land overgrown with bracken. George was given two years rent-free and then paid £40 a year, which was a good enough spec for him to marry and they had twenty children. His wife died, he married again and another two children arrived — of whom Jack was one — to be fed and nurtured out of 174 acres, most of which were rough with only some 60 acres under cultivation.

There was no need for hired help, there were more than enough lads and their day started early; father George and wife slept on the first floor, the lads in the attic above and there was communication between for George had a rope attached to a bell in the attic which he tugged at 5 a.m. If the lads weren't down and ready for work before him, there was trouble. As the lads grew they went into farm place, or as keepers to earn a little money which they were expected to send home. The girls were busy around the house — and nothing much changed in the following generation; oil lamps for light, water to be brought in buckets from a spring in the field for the large family's everyday use and on butter-making days an extra expedition to a spring even further away where the water was cooler and cleaner. All to be done before going off to school at 7.30 a.m.

Monday was wash day and with so many in the family there was much to do, water to be brought, the boiler to light in the outhouse, and the pounding with a wooden posser, up and down on the clothes and sheets. There was the mangle with its wooden rollers and cast iron handle, and the all-enveloping steam and smell of wet clothes. A good drying day was possible on the edge of the moors, but wet Mondays must have been horrendous. Even then there was the ironing, with the irons being heated and re-heated on the turve fire.

America Jack was born when his father was sixty-five years old and by the age of eleven he was working on the farm and, as his sister said, never had time to play. He and his two young sisters,

Gladys and Dorothy, had their tasks to do, feeding the calves, ducks and hens, turning the churn, scrubbing out the dairy and many other jobs — snagging turnips, picking potatoes, cleaning out the cow byres, mucking out the pigs. Their mother was busy with breakfasts, ten o'clocks to take out to the fields, dinner to cook and do.

America Jack was a handy lad. He could make a whistle from a piece of ash as thick as your finger, nick it round, cut a "V" in it, soak it in water when the skin slid off, then whittle it to shape and you had a whistle. Later on he used the tip of a cow or sheep horn. He didn't buy a skep to feed the cattle; he made them from being quite young. He would split four strips off a length of straight hazel, the thick centre remaining made the beams that went across, and he used a thick briar for the circular parts with the ends shaved off, lapped over and fastened with three little nails. He tied a string across this to pull it into oval shape and hung it up to dry, after which he started with the bows and windings, using the thin strips.

Food was basic. "If you had bread and a bit of margarine on it you didn't have jam as well. Or you could have dry bread and jam," so his sister told me. Margarine on a farm needs explanation — cash producing products from the farm included butter, curds and eggs, and butter was not for the family. For years rabbits and an occasional hare were the staple meat, potatoes and turnips were both eaten and sold. America Jack's mother Mary, and the children who were old enough, milked the eight or nine cows, churned the butter and made the curds. A few hens produced eggs but they didn't lay many because there wasn't money to buy proper feed and the land "had nothing in it for them". A few chickens now and then but they were never very plump.

Whatever there was went to Whitby on Saturday. Mrs Welford, with one of the children beside her, set off with a pony and trap at seven o'clock in the morning down the rough track from the farm, along the lane to the main road, over the top to Lythe and then down 1 in 4 Lythe bank where they dismounted to ease the pony, and on to Whitby. The pony was stabled for the day either in Black Horse Yard in Church Street, or Price's stables in Silver Street. Money was so short that frequently the sixpence charged for stabling could not be paid until the produce was sold; a good rabbit might fetch sixpence, extra good might fetch ninepence, curds were twopence for a large measure. "We always had two geese and a gander and used to rear some goslings to sell at Christmas. We also had a few ducks but feed was a problem — they didn't dress out right, they weren't as good as they should have been, the feathers weren't properly up so that you couldn't pluck them properly."

There was one Saturday when America Jack accompanied his mother and when he went to collect the pony at the end of the day he was told it wasn't ready.

"Not ready?" said Jack, "I only left it for stabling."

The stableman made more excuses — to try and cover the fact that the animal was not there. Jack was not to be put off.

"Let me see it, then," he said.

"You can't just now," said the stableman.

Jack, getting nowhere, did what most lads would do — he went round the corner and watched. Sure enough, after a while, his horse came up the street, in the shafts of a funeral hearse.

Luckily America had a sense of humour; his sisters say he was a mischief and a torment. One said, "When I was seventeen or eighteen I used to go dancing at Roxby or Ugthorpe, three or four miles away and the dances didn't finish till two in the morning. A lad would escort me back over the moor to the top gate of the farm and I would run down through the fields to America House. We had an earth closet at the bottom of the garden but even after that long walk I daren't use it at 3 a.m. But in those days there was always a chamber pot under the bed, so it was a matter of straight in the front

John (America Jack) Welford, of America House Farm, Newton Mulgrave, Hinderwell.

door, upstairs to the bedroom — and this time I dived under the bed for the chamber and it wasn't there; Jack had replaced it with an egg cup."

He wasn't a lad for the girls, he never courted anyone but Phyllis Brown, the daughter of an ironstone miner from Scaling who was working at Harrison's farm at Borrowby. He went courting on horseback and then went walking with Phyllis over the moors. They married in 1928 — no honeymoon but straight back to America House and work. Father George died seven years later aged 84, and until only a few months before his death was issuing orders, one of the breed of men whose word was law, whose families treated them with respect and some awe and who delegated responsibility to no-one. The eldest son should have taken over the tenancy but because of his longevity all the older sons from his first marriage had long since left and Jack took over.

At last Jack had the chance to make improvements and with the start of the Second World War in 1939 there were grants available from the "War Ag" to bring more land into production. Previously there had only been fifty or sixty acres of useable land but the wartime half-grant meant the reclamation of upwards of a hundred acres which was re-seeded and now grows grass.

But in wartime it was not grass that was needed; it was corn and crops to feed the population, the farmer had no choice in what he grew. The War Ag team moved in with caterpillar tractors to plough up rough land which had never been broken in living memory; those tractors had far more power than horses, their single furrow ploughs dug deeper, and at America House they brought to the surface large boulders which could only be removed by blasting them apart with black powder. One field does have a quarry in it and it became obvious that fields on the edge of the moor were a continuation of it.

Circumstances helped America Jack. The pressure for food in wartime brought improvements that his father could never have afforded. he took over at a time when you could sell everything you could produce. He is reported to have remarked to a visiting Agricultural Minister after the war ended, "I did kill a lot of sheep in those days, they kept breaking legs, you know. All I could do was kill them . . ." with a twinkle in his eye that deceived no-one.

After years of having to do as he was told it was now up to Jack to make decisions — and like his father he appeared to find it difficult to delegate. Money was more plentiful and he made things easier for his wife and family — an inside water supply, an Aga cooker, a washing machine, and in 1956 came electricity. Jack told the tale of how the Electricity Board produced a scheme where, for a flat payment of £160, they would bring power to any farm. America House was two and a half miles from the nearest point at Ellerby, "so", said he, "they lost out badly on that one."

So much for the man and his background; his main preoccupation was with his flock of 570 head of black faced sheep, two-thirds of which were on the moor stray beside the Whitby-Middlesbrough road. Traffic on the road brought casualties, added to which was the drop in the number of other flocks on the moor leaving gaps which the remaining flocks tended to fill. There used to be four flocks between Ugthorpe Rails and Skelder Top and now there are none. The sheep looked for the roadside grass which was sweetest — a flock in a neighbouring stray would have eaten their grass and there would not have been the attraction for another flock to move into their territory but without them Jack's sheep could wander for miles. He had the additional problem of the road cutting across the moor from Calais House on the Middlesbrough road to Lythe on the coast road which allowed his sheep, particularly in spring, to wander into the villages of Ellerby and Mickleby where they got into gardens. America Jack's first solution was to tether two sheep dogs, one each side of the road, with fences to steer the sheep towards them, but sheep are cunning and they soon learned that if they walked up the centre of the road the dogs could not reach them. After three years the Council decided to fit a cattle grid and Jack had to find £600 towards the total of £1,800 — which took a bit of finding but saved a lot of work. Even then there were incidents of cunning sheep lying down and rolling over the grid to get to the other side!

So summer was a busy time, early mornings and late nights shepherding on his Cleveland Bay mare; his familiar figure could be seen at half past five in the morning with his dogs shepherding the sheep and lambs back from the road but even so a number were killed. With a grown ewe worth £40 and upwards in his day, and little hope of finding the offending motorist, it was a worthwhile exercise. Just after the war a ewe might fetch £1.50, a lamb five shillings (25p) and that price would be accepted. "At four shillings you would take it back home."

Man and horse worked together; to see him lean from the saddle and lift an ailing ewe up over the pommel to take it home was a sight to remember. Land Rovers, he maintained, were lower, they tied you to the roads and paths and were no substitute. Up on his horse he could see if his sheep had moved off.

Sheep shearing days were long and thirsty. Apart from experienced shearers who swung the sheep on its back in one swift movement, held it down with one hand and sheared off the fleece with the other, there were beginners who had to learn the hard way — for them and for the sheep. America Jack watched as one lad clipped away and nipped the flesh — and clipped some more and nipped some more "Have you finished?" said Jack. "Are you going home for the weekend?"

"Yes," said the lad, "I am."

"Well," said Jack, "take that fleece with you, and the meat on it will see you and your old man and woman over the weekend for your Sunday dinner."

Haymaking and threshing days brought in the neighbours to help on a tit-for-tat basis until the sons were of an age to help. There were rabbiting days when the elder children and men with a couple of guns and plenty of ferrets would spend a winter's day in the fields. "You didn't get much done before lunch and it was dark by four o'clock, but you could get eighty rabbits in a day, the farms were wick with them, and maybe get a shilling apiece for them. We used to hang them on fences as we went along and go back with a horse and cart to collect them up. Then you had to paunch them — and if you hadn't had your tea before you started, you didn't want it afterwards."

And there were "conversation days". America Jack loved a natter with old friends and an hour's visit could easily spread to half a day or more. Jack, and George Southgate who lived at a neighbouring farm, would be at it all evening and, still deep in conversation, one would set the other back home. On one occasion, when neither was back home by three in the morning, search parties went out only to find the pair contentedly sitting under a hedge oblivious to time.

One oft-told tale of America Jack is that he had a flock of sheep to drive from Sandsend, three miles north of Whitby on the coast road, to a field on the outskirts of town. It was midsummer and traffic was heavy but Jack and two dogs took no notice whatsoever — sheep were there before motor cars! As the sheep entered Whitby some of them strayed into a garden and the lady of the house came out to see her precious plants disappearing.

She said, "Someone will have to pay. Are these your sheep?"

Jack, with his most innocent look, said, "No, they belong to Eddie Cummin at the Midland Bank."

Mr. Cummin was not only Jack's bank manager but also treasurer of the Cleveland Bay Horse Society, so when an irate lady phoned him about the damage caused by "his" sheep he had a shrewd idea as to who was behind it. Jack, as usual, had the last word, "Well, Eddie has my overdraft so he must own them."

America Jack was a stalwart of the Cleveland Bay Horse Society, and was an acknowledged expert in dealing with recalcitrant animals as is related in a later chapter. Naturally, therefore, he also dealt in horses. The classic story must be of the contest between him and Rob Rudd. In the late 1930s Rob lived with his father Sol at Beggar-Me-Neighbour Stud, Stokesley. He had heard on the grapevine that America Jack had a Cleveland Bay stallion for sale and decided to pay him a visit. Before he left home his father said, "Don't let on that it's you that wants the horse or he'll bump up the price. Let him think you're looking for it for somebody else, sort of feeling the way, like."

So Rob left home in Stokesley early one morning by bus — few people had cars in those days — changed at Great Ayton, then at Guisborough, Skelton and Loftus and finally arrived mid-morning at Hinderwell to walk over the fields to America House. When he arrived he was told Jack and the lads were in the top field hoeing turnips and, sure enough, when he found America he was busy hoeing away.

"Now then, Rob," said Jack, "what can I do for you? You can see we're kind of busy."

"Well," said Rob, "a certain party said you might be interested in selling a Cleveland Bay stallion. If you are, I might know someone who is interested. Is it right? have you a horse?"

"I might have," said Jack, hoeing away at his turnips.

"Can I see it then?" said Rob.

"Well, you'll have to wait till I get to the end of the row."

So Rob and Jack exchanged pleasantries and eventually after the row was completed they left the field to view the horse. It was caught and inspected and Jack was eventually asked the price.

Jack said, "If I was selling it — and I'm not saying that I am — for a horse like that I would want £35 before parting."

Rob said, "If I was interested — and I'm not saying I am — you'll have to come again. I never heard tell of such a price in my life."

The conversation was cut short by America's wife Phyllis calling that it was dinner time. "You'll come in and have a bite of dinner with us, then, Rob?

After dinner there was talk of "Will it yoke?" and the stallion was geared up and taken up the turnip field to scruffle the rows. Rob was handed the reins and while he went up and down the field Jack and the lads went back to their hoeing. And then the real haggling began; Rob, still maintaining that he was only half interested in buying, would make an offer. Jack, still insisting that he really didn't want to sell, would reject it, and so it went on and on, up and down the rows until milking time when Jack said, "It's no good, we'll have to knock off now."

The haggling went on right through milking, then it was teatime, then back to the turnip field; as the evening progressed the gap between Jack's asking price and Rob's offers gradually decreased but they were nowhere near making a deal. Then it was supper time — "and you'll come in and have a bite of supper with us?" said Jack. And the time came and went for Rob to catch his bus back to Stokesley — no bargain made and he set off to walk home. To show there were no hard feelings Jack walked with him to the moor gate above the farm where they stood for quite a while talking prices and finally parted with the gap reduced to One Pound with neither man giving way.

So Rob set off across the moor to Calais House, on to Danby Beacon, across the turnpike road to Commondale and Kildale and back to Stokesley which, as the crow flies, is about sixteen miles. Somewhere on that long walk Rob decided to give Jack that other pound and the following morning he returned by bus to America House, gave Jack the money and triumphantly rode the stallion back to Beggar-Me-Neighbour Stud.

Jack's other attribute was as a poet — or writer of scurrilous verses as those who featured in them would put it; hardly an incident occurred but, at the most inopportune moment, an anonymous poem

America Jack Welford on his Cleveland Bay mare, a familiar sight on the moors near Scaling Dam. 1956.

A string of Cleveland Bays loaded as the pack horses which travelled from village to village before main roads were built. America Jack is on the lead horse.

would be circulated — and many are treasured to this day. Always there was an element of truth so the subject could never completely deny it but inevitably the worst possible interpretation of the most innocent occurrence was implied. As you will realise, the following incident, with Jack actually involved, was one such occasion; it concerns a certain young lady in the Whitby area who, one spring, bought a Cleveland Bay mare intending to ride her. Shortly afterwards she obtained a temporary job at Castle Howard as secretary so she arranged for the mare to run on a farm in the area and, in a year when grass was short, bought forty bales of hay as additional feed and had it delivered to the farm. At the end of the summer the job finished, she returned to Whitby with the mare and the balance of the forty bales remained near Castle Howard.

In consultation with America Jack she decided that the mare should have a foal and there was some discussion as to which stallion was suitable; the decision was made that one in Nottinghamshire looked likely and she and Jack set off to have a look at him. On the way the question of what to do with the bales of hay was discussed and Jack opined, "Either they come back home or maybe the stallion owner will take them as part payment for service; it's six of one and half a dozen of the other where we move them."

Our young lady thought it was a good idea and after the stallion had been inspected and approved, she suddenly asked the stallion man if he would "take part payment in kind".

Said Jack, "The man thought he was on a good thing and beamed all over his face. She suddenly realised what she had said and turned all shades from pink to purple."

Snow-clearing at Glaisdale in 1956.

Above: Norman Nellis, one of several brothers who were the backbone of horse shows in Whitby district, with his agricultural horses, Darkie and Prince. August 1961 at Hinderwell.

Opposite, top: Henry Peirson, of Echo Hill, Sleights, going sledging with a pair of his horses in 1960.

Opposite, bottom: Ploughing match at Bannial Flat, near Whitby, 1958. It is not only the judges who have expert opinions.

Sad moment for Joe Summerson, of Ellerby, near Whitby, in February 1964 when he parted with his horses.

Joe Summerson, after finally saying goodbye to his horses and retiring to his farmhouse kitchen.

TOM MORLEY OF BROCK HALL

THE late Tom Morley, of Brock Hall, near Boggle Hole, Robin Hood's Bay, south of Whitby, married in 1923 and when he gave me an interview in 1981, said they'd had a family of four lads and three lasses. Two were at home, one at Browside Farm, another at Fyling Hall Farm, all farming or married to farmers except for one daughter "who married a man who works at I.C.I. and he has a collar and tie job". Over the years their land had expanded to 488 acres, including Brock Hall, most of St. Ives, Fyling Hall and Browside; there were 100 beef cows and calves were reared right through till they were sold off fat. Milk production had stopped in 1976.

Listening to him was to be given a history lesson in farming as it used to be when, he said, "it was all hoss work and hand work, far worse than now when machinery takes all the hard work out of farming".

"There was a lot of pleasure in working with horses, a lot, a lot. Ploughing was a job I liked, as good a job as any on the farm. You could go away to plough with a pair of horses and you had something to speak to and talk to all day long. Now you get sat on a tractor and it's all buzz, buzz, buzz. You'd do very well if you ploughed an acre a day and at the back end of the year you wouldn't manage that. T'auld farmers thought you were doing all right at an acre a day."Nowadays in this part of the country with tractors they can get through ten acres "if you go in a morning and stop until night and you mean it".

Is it ploughed as well?

"The majority of people would say it was, but I say it isn't."

But it must be an advantage at the end of the day when you can just switch the tractor off?

"Now you're asking! When you'd finished at dusk, you'd been ploughing as long as you could see, you'd come home with the two hosses you'd been working with and there'd be another four or five in the stable and they were all to do. Ungear your horses, feed 'em, clean out and by then you'd come in for your supper around six o'clock. If you weren't finished you went out and finished them off afterwards.

"You'd spend the evening playing cards or dominoes — there was no other entertainment — until 8 o'clock when you went out and stabled up, took 'em down to the trough to water, bed 'em up and feed them. By then it was getting on for 9 o'clock and the old man would want you off to bed — he'd say, 'It's about bedtime isn't it, or you won't be ready in the morning.' And next morning his father used to come on the landing before it was daylight and be shouting for him. Then he'd go down in the yard and it wouldn't be long before he was shouting again, 'Are you going to be all b . . . day?'

I asked what staff his father had on the farm before Tom and his brothers were old enough to work: "He hired a man and a strong lad, and a great strong lass to help mother — she also had to go out morning and night to help milk the cows, and nine days out of ten she had young calves to feed with a bucket. The strong lad, maybe 16 or 17 years old, helped with the bullocks and that side of things, and it was his job to take out a spare pair of horses if they were wanted. The hired man dealt with the horses and the stack work."

What sort of wages were they paid?

"The man who could do anything had £21 a year. the strong lad had about £16 a year. The strong lass who worked all the hours that God sent would have about £12 a year. He got them at the hirings — if he didn't get fixed up at Whitby he went on to Egton and I oft times went with him. T'awd farmer would go up to them and strike a bargain, sae munny pounds fer't year, and then give 'em a hiring penny which was then either half a crown or five bob to fasten the bargain. They were paid on Martinmas Day, 23rd November, and then went for a week's holiday. If they'd drawn anything during the year, that was knocked off. But if they'd needed a new pair of boots that was only a few shillings, a new suit was a quid or twenty-five bob."

"When they got paid, our old feller thought he'd given them all the money in the world. I don't know what he'd think if he came back now! When I was a lad going to school there was a chap lived and worked here for seven years — he finished his time with John Collinson — and he used to give me sixpence every week to go to Anderson's shop in Thorpe for an ounce of thin brown twist tobacco which was threepence ha'penny, and a packet of twelve boxes of matches which was three ha'pence the lot, and I had a penny change. And Fred used to say to me sometimes — not always, mind you — you can keep that this time, but it didn't happen oft. Well, I could go to school for the next week with as many toffees as I could eat!"

In 1953, about fifty years later, minimum wages had risen for males, for a 47-hour week, to £6 for over twenty-ones; females received £4.11s.0d. Holidays were at the rate of one day for each month in the year.

Brock Hall Farm was part of the Fyling Hall Estate — of which the Big House is now a private school and the land sold off. When Tom Morley's father came to Brock Hall the estate belonged to John Wharram Barry, described by Tom as "a stiff little chap, always rigged up like a gentleman, white scarf with a gold pin, yellow leather leggings with a strap around them and buckled at the top; polished leather boots. He always wore a hard hat and always had a terrier dog with him which roamed ahead of him as he went round the estate. A lot of the masons and other workers — who weren't over keen on work in them days — used to keep an eye out and the dog gave them ten minutes warning."

If his description gives an impression of a fiery little man who ruled the area this is borne out by the Robin Hood's Bay-born novelist Leo Walmsley in his book where he recounts being very frightened by the local squire.

Tom Morley was in no doubt as to Barry's influence. "We were still at school and after we finished about four o'clock time, I'll bet you would meet him between Gilsom Bank Top and Fyling Hall. You had to raise your cap and the lasses had to curtsey, and I'll bet if you didn't the school gaffer would know next morning and you'd be lucky if you didn't get the cane. I daren't tell father when I got home because he'd say, 'You deserve it and I'll give you some more'."

Tom had earlier recounted how his father had originally been tenant of Greenland Farm, Goathland, and that there was a year between moving from there to Brock Hall, which was spent at Tom's grandmother's pub at Littlebeck. This was and is a strong centre of Methodism, principally Tom averred because of the Ventress family who farm there. "You were expected to go and everybody went including some queer ones; there was one, Bob Gray, who used to take a lot of drink, and the services were in the afternoon after the lunchtime session. Old Henry Ventress used to sit right against the parson in the pulpit and he had a desperate habit of creeping around the pews during the prayers and asking folk if they'd found Jesus. One time when I was there he landed up against Bob Gray. 'Have you found Jesus?' said Henry. 'No,' said Bob. 'I ain't. Is he lost?' "

From another source came another story of Littlebeck; the pub, just across the stream from the chapel, became a private house and is occupied by Mr Tom Whittaker, the "Gnome Man" wood carver, The period would be around 1950 when two young daughters were at home and learning to play the piano, an instrument which, they and his wife complained, was long past its best and fit for nothing but firewood. The family went away for the weekend and Tom Whittaker, having nothing particular to do, decided to demolish it. By Sunday lunch time he had reduced the wood case to firewood and was left with the frame full of strings. After a strengthening sandwich and a drink he dragged the frame out of the door on to the grass to set about it with a sledgehammer. He said, with an expression on his face as impish as the gnome he carves on his work, "It was chapel-time, and they were just starting the first hymn when I struck. The singing faltered and died. It was, I imagine, somewhat like the sound of the Lost Chord."

The Morleys moved to Brock Hall with Tom five or six years old. Down the road another mile or so at the mouth of a wide stream is the North Sea; on the left at the mouth of the stream is Boggle Hole, now a Youth Hostel but at that time it was Bay Mill, used by farmers from the low side of Robin Hood's Bay — those from the north side used Ramsdale Mill. Jim Hutton was the miller at Bay Mill and ground the corn to feed pigs and bullocks, and sold flour and other feed. As Tom said, "There weren't engines on the farms in those days". The mill continued into the 1930s. The road to it was on the right-hand side of the stream and he used to take a horse and cart down there, across the beach and stream and up to the mill, tides and stormy seas permitting!

Brock Hall had 129 acres. The rent was £82 a year, paid in two halves in February and August in Whitby, "and it took some finding. Nowadays you can let summer grass for grazing at £40 to £50 an acre. That's how things have changed."

The February rent was raised by "keeping a concern of pigs which we used to kill in January". Whilst he was talking I remembered seeing a series of photographs of pig killing, taken by Thomas Watson, the Lythe photographer, around 1920; the whole procedure took place at the side of the village street, with the deed being done with a spike and large mallet, then tipping the carcass into a large tin bath of hot water before scraping off the hair and butchering into joints. Tom Morley agreed that that was about it, and that the flavour of the chitterlings and scraps was a flavoursome memory.

"The barn would be full of sides of fat bacon pigs — they wouldn't bother to kill them unless they weighed around 25 stone. Now they will kill them at 14 stone; the old lads wouldn't have thought they were worth killing. The pigs went to the curers for salting, ours went to my uncle Tom Welford in Thorpe, or sometimes to Spaven's in Whitby who sold them out Leeds way." Spaven's used to have extensive warehouses in Bagdale with a shop where they sold farming equipment and seed. Tom said they used to get around 4s.6d. (22p) a stone stripped; neither head, feet, liver or anything else was included. He said that in the 1980s a young pig raised for bacon would fetch around £20 in the mart before it's started on.

Feeding methods were different altogether. "The February pigs were fed on barley meal and boiled taties and sweet turnips, all grown on the farm. Now there's all kinds of fancy foods but bacon doesn't taste the same; it's all through the feeding. It's the same with beef; bullocks had much the same diet as the pigs but it wasn't boiled. The beef tasted sweet and juicy and much nicer than today with all the artificial feed. But it produces a bigger beast more quickly and that's why it's done. The same with calves — there was no suckling them, the milk was separated and fed from a bucket. The cream went for butter which went to market to pay for the groceries and maybe a joint of beef.

"I've no time for battery eggs. A neighbour of ours filled all his buildings with wire pens and, by gum, he got some eggs. A few times he brought us a box full but the yolks were pale and they tasted of fish — which is what they were fed on! I didn't like them at all compared with those we got from our own few running around the yard." What would Tom have made of the 1989 situation with strange diseases and stranger regulations? He would doubtless have made some "Curried" comments.

The discussion then returned to the subject of rent and the second instalment due in August, for which a few bullocks were sold. "Quite a few," said Tom, "for in my early days, after my father's time, we were selling two-year old beasts for £9 a time. George Wellburn was the main buyer of stock around here and he used to come round buying; he used to spend a lot of time — he was a hard man to deal with and so were the farmers — and I've known him come here two or three times before he got five or six bullocks bought. He didn't send transport to collect them, his trucking place was Ruswarp and what do's we used to have driving the beasts there."

Six bullocks to drive from Brock Hall to Ruswarp, eight miles away, meant an early start. Three horses for three old men and as many lads as could be mustered, beasts protesting at being separated from the rest and already steaming. Up the lane to the main road wasn't too bad with the animals contained by hedges, a rider in front, lads on the flanks and two more horsemen behind. The thing to do was keep them moving. Tom said, "Once they were on the open road we lads used to be running all over the moor till you were fair busting, and the old men used to be galloping on ponies to turn the cattle. The thing not to do was let them look back where they'd come from, if they got a smell of home that was it. If they got a glance back at the top of Kirkmoor Beck they would break back as hard as they could gallop. And you'd have to have another go and maybe another after that."

That wasn't the only hazard. There were other farmers driving their beasts to the same place and woe betide if the groups met. The beasts would have smelt each other before the men saw, and within seconds they'd be fighting, rearing up, butting and mixing it while men swore and lads pushed and shoved to separate their own without letting any get away. Men prevailed, the unruly mob was hassled in the right direction and kept going. "Go easy with the sticks, lads, you'll bruise 'em and he'll knock the price down."

As Tom said, "They were steaming and we were sweating; we did get to Ruswarp but I reckon they'd lose a bit of weight on the way."

When I recorded the conversation with Mr Morley he was well into his eighties but still very much in control of what went on on the farms, and of the purse strings. I had made an appointment and he was ready for me when I arrived, but tales are told of representatives who arrived unannounced and were subject to a little delay. One told me that it was very unwise to start to talk business immediately; there were formalities to go through, the weather to discuss, the state of prices at the mart to bemoan until the moment came when he said, "Now lad, you'll be wanting an order."

Pity, then, the fertiliser salesman, for, as Tom said, "The amount of artificial we put on the land amazes me. Just today I paid the traveller just sixty pounds short of £3,000 for our three farms, and there's more to come, maybe another £2,000 worth, and that will just about do for grass and corn this summer. I remember when it wasn't there to buy in father's time; there was plenty of lime and basic slag, and later Superphosphate, but that was about it. There was as good crops grown then as there is today. We've a foldyard which holds 167 cows and calves; it's cleaned out, not with shovel

Thatching at Ainthorpe.

Frank and Norman Nellis of Whitby laying a hedge.

and brush like it used to be but with a scraper on the tractor, and two trailer loads go out on the land every morning. There's another foldyard with about a hundred in there, bedded up all winter and led out in the spring. We're spreading as much — and more — natural manure as we used to do, but they say we still need artificial. I grumble about it but its no use. It gets paid for but I sometimes wonder how the devil it does . . ."

Now, as I write, the story is all of ten per cent and twenty per cent land to lie fallow because of the grain mountains and overproduction, and less artificial fertilisers in an attempt to cut back production. But, as one commentator said, farmers want to keep on farming and you can be very sure that it won't take long before production is just as high on the few acres.

CATTLE, PIGS AND GEESE

Highland cattle in snow at the Delves, Egton Bridge, in March 1963.

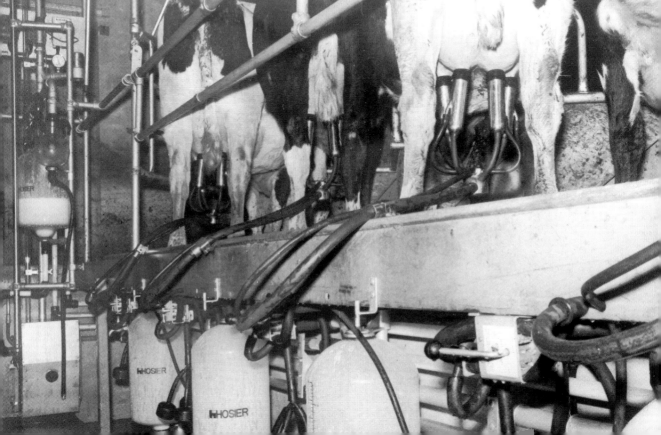

Above: *Ruswarp Mart at Christmas 1965 when, as usual, the prices were escalating as butchers vied for the prize-winning beasts and the tickets to display in their shop windows. Farmers faces probably mirror the anxiety as to whose would win and get top price.*

Opposite, top: *Tom Harland's bull at Newton Mulgrave. The author had completed photographing the prize herd of cows when Mr. Harland asked for one of his bull, which was running loose. It is best to photograph animals standing on the flat or slightly uphill, and the bull was standing downhill — which I pointed out. Mr. Harland walked across and poked the bull in the ribs with his walking stick — whilst I looked over my shoulder for the nearest line of escape!*

Opposite, bottom: *One of the first Milking Parlours in the Whitby district was installed at Wilk's Farm, Lealholm, in December 1971. Memorable to the author because a representative of the equipment suppliers arrived in a light grey suit and lingered a little too long in the parlour after the cows were let in . . . !*

Near Robin Hood's Bay — where's the bed?

A good flock for Christmas — at Matthew Stevenson's farm, Saltwick Bay, in 1949.

LEO WELFORD and NELSON HUTTON

A DESCRIPTION of the life and times of Leo Welford will confirm some of Tom Morley's comments. Mr Welford, much the same vintage, was born at Wood Hall Farm, Lealholm, where his father was tenant. He was born into a generation when lads were kept in petticoats until the age of four — and he had an old photograph to prove it. In 1906, at the age of eight, the family moved to a little farm at the Presbytery, Ugthorpe and he described how he went to school there with his dinner bag — no school meals provided, nor were there any fancy subjects taught, just the three R's, Reading, Writing and Arithmetic. In 1928 he started at Frankland Farm, Ugthorpe, 28 acres and times were so hard for the next three years that when he saw a job advertised at £5 a week he very nearly gave up farming and took it.

They survived and in 1933 he and his wife moved to Hinderwell where they had 57 acres plus a few odd fields around the village. For a time bankruptcy was a real possibility but things gradually improved on the mixed farm which included a milk round. Leo tells that one field was behind the Brown Cow Inn in the village, and there was a bungalow occupied by a lady next to the field. "Without asking me or telling me she put up a clothes line in the field and one day, as I arrived, a pair of her 'smalls' were disappearing inside a cow — it had pulled it off the line. It didn't do the beast any harm but the lady came out and played up hell with me!"

They stayed for eleven hard years. The price of beasts was low: "My stirks, 13 months old and milk reared, were fetching under £6 apiece, and I remember when some two-year old bullocks from Frank Raw at Ugthorpe sold at Ruswarp Mart for £13 apiece. I can remember a Christmas when we'd paid all our bills and the children crying because there just wasn't anything left to buy presents. One of my milk customers owed me £8 but they were as badly off as me and there was no point in asking for it.

"The upturn came when Ramshaws of Redcar started collecting milk, the beginnings of the Milk Board. Frank Gill and I were the first two in our area and the first cheque was at 5d (under 2p) a gallon, but that was better than we'd been getting. We were selling on the doorstep for threepence a pint and I continued door to door deliveries; we always gave a pint and another dip for good measure and there were a lot of objections when the bottles came in because they were only getting a bare pint."

"The milk went through a cooler, it wasn't filtered, but I never had any complaints from customers," said Mr Welford. The author recalls, about that time, being conducted around William Cox's milk plant which used to be at the bottom end of Church Street, Whitby, in premises now occupied by the Electricity Board and which continued for some years after the war, when it was taken over by Co-operative Creameries; I remember very well the raw milk being tipped from the churns to pass through the first filter, and the amazing amount of unpalatable-looking residue that showed up. But generations of us drank "fresh" milk and enjoyed it and seemed none the worse for it. Who was it said that we all swallowed a peck of dirt in a lifetime?

Mr Welford went on, "There were a lot of complaints when the price went up by a halfpenny a pint — one customer said, 'You farmers, you're always making big profits,' but by then it was the Milk Marketing Board that set the price." When the war came there were lots of new regulations and permits and some poorer families with small children had a permit for a free allowance of milk. "There was one family who were getting three free pints a week on permit from the Food Office in Whitby. Any extra she paid for and that was usually two extra halfpints for baking. The price went up one penny — so her total milk bill became threepence a week. She was in the village shop, which was full of people when I went in and she said, 'Bloody farmers', but I didn't spill the beans on how much she was getting for nowt!"

Whitby's wartime Food Office had several homes — the first was over the public lavatories in New Quay Road — before it settled in the old Congregational Mission Hall in Silver Street. As with many things in 1939 the recruitment of experienced staff was an impossibility and there were a few strange decisions. From the Food Office was collected the ration book, an essential document obtainable only on production of your Identity Card. The coupons were named — one ounce (30g) of cheese per week, half a pound of sugar per week, and the butter ration varied down to as low as two ounces a week in 1941. Milk varied with the season from half a pint a week upwards for adults and that problem was compounded by the shortage of feed stuffs in the early years which caused the slaughter of dairy cows.So far as the farming community was concerned the formation of the War Agricultural Committees to oversee and improve production seemed an interference with traditional methods and the Man from the Ministry was not welcomed. But with much of our food coming from overseas and with the ever growing threat of submarine action which grew to decimate some of the convoys of ships, so that by early 1941 ships were being sunk at the rate of three a day, it was essential to increase home production. An early step was an offer of £2 an acre to plough up grassland, which in the case of Mr Robert Harland of Newton Mulgrave meant ploughing up fields undisturbed for many years because they were full of large stones and which were in fact the foundations of the old township of Newton Mulgrave, long disappeared and otherwise remembered only by an inscribed stone on one remaining building. Conservation had not reared its head at that time and in wartime one has the feeling that even relics of the Ancient Britons were of less import than feeding the population.

The slogan was "Digging for Victory". Pasture land, public parks, lawns and common land were ploughed up. School playing fields were planted and tended by the children. Many farm workers were called up for the Forces and were replaced by the Women's Land Army, 80,000 strong — many of whom, who in pre-war days had never worked outside their homes, found they enjoyed it and particularly the sense of freedom the wages gave them. This labour force was augmented with Conscientious Objectors who were given the option of doing essential work, and also after a year or two by 40,000 Italian and German prisoners of war. The general population was also doing its bit — a few kept pigs and many kept chickens which were fed on a smelly mixture of scraps, potato peelings, carrot tops and sprout leaves, with their own egg shells ground up for grit. There were pig swill bins on street corners and there was a collection service from restaurants and cafes. Very little was wasted.

Apart from setting up local Food Offices there were national campaigns; the Radio Doctor gave hints on healthy diets, aluminium pans were needed to build Spitfires, iron railings were cut down to provide steel for tanks and there were campaigns to save water. Music Hall veterans Elsie and Doris Waters featured on radio giving hints on how to make dried egg and spam into savoury dishes. Dried egg was imported from the U.S.A. because fresh eggs contain 5/6ths water which took up valuable shipping space. It was rationed at one pack, equal to one dozen eggs, every two months. "Food Flashes" and "Kitchen Front" broadcasts advocated raw carrots for sweetening jams and puddings, while swedes, turnips with carrots and potatoes covered by a potato flour crust made up the much vaunted "Woolton Pie" — Lord Woolton was a Minister of Food, but what a way to be remembered! Fish, game, fruit and vegetables were never rationed but imported fruits like oranges were reserved for children — or available to special customers "Under the Counter", a phrase which irritated the many who were not favoured. Bananas disappeared completely and children only knew them from pictures in books.

Butchers were generally courted by the public and universally suspected of "Under the Counter" dealings; side door transactions after closing time, the barter of tins of fruit from the greengrocer's allocation in return for a leg of lamb, the quiet disposal of the odd ham from an illicitly kept pig, the extra bit of this and that for friends or relatives, all were laid at the butcher's door. Mr Mannering's bits of steak wrapped in newspaper from Corporal Jones in "Dad's Army" summed up the situation.

Probably one of the least popular wartime foods was the national Wholemeal Bread Loaf which used flour of 85 per cent extraction, saving grain imports and shipping space, but which nowadays would, as then, be promoted as far better for us than the attractive white flour. Various diets were recommended, the ingredients depending on whatever was in best supply, but some were just too much. Winston Churchill's opinion was poured forth in a letter to his Ministry of Food when he wrote, "Almost all the food faddists I have known, nut-eaters and the like, have died young after a long period of senile decay."

Then there were the perennial arguments with Argentina (who supported the Germans) over the price of their Corned Beef. No wonder our farmers were asked to boost production and tempted with subsidies to move into intensive farming and the use of chemical fertilisers. Fuel for tractors and essential farm work was given priority but dyed red; there had been a ration of petrol generally until 1942 when it was reserved for essential users. Within a year or two some of those who had cars were tempted when it was found that the red dye in commercial petrol could be removed by passing it through the filter in the gas masks with which everyone had been issued at the beginning of hostilities; but there was the strong likelihood of being stopped and asked where you were going, and a few prison sentences were imposed.

Mr O.C. (Ted) Atkinson was the Ministry Man for farms in the Whitby area and he remained to farm at Egton after hostilities were over; he was assisted in his wartime work by experienced local farmers who could be persuaded to take on an unpopular job which was mainly visiting farms "under supervision" by the Ministry as not being efficient producers. The War Agricultural Committees set targets for each county; farms were graded for efficiency, ten per cent being graded top class "A", the moderately good were "B", and the ones to be given special attention were Grade "C" which were visited by War Ag. officers and told to pull their socks up. In a few cases farmers were evicted and the War Ag. took over the land.

One of those who was asked to help was Mr Tom Morley of Brock Hall, who said, "I had had six years on the Whitby Rural District Council but I turned tired of that lark — what were we there for? Whatever we discussed had to go for decision to Northallerton so we were wasting our time. Then I had four years on the War Ag. as Husbandry Officer, which turned out to be right into my line of business. I was nervous at first but I thought I would try it, and I was pleased I did. Some of the farms we visited which were under supervision taught me a lot — you could learn from them, things you didn't know yourself. I was supposed to visit these farms every month, then report to the Whitby committee and again to Northallerton where they sat two or three times a month."

"It wouldn't make you very popular?"

"There's a lot of people said that to me but, do you know, after the war finished and travellers were going round the farms, often they were asked if I was still at Brock Hall and that they'd like to see me again. That didn't give a bad account of me, did it? About the first farm I visited, up the Dales, I went with Ted Atkinson, the Ministry Man, and they'd had a lot of bother with this chap. It was a good farm, right on the edge of the moor. On the way up Ted said, 'By gum, you're going to meet a queer feller today.'

" 'I've met some queer fellers before,' I thought. But when we walked down the stable yard I could see this great tall rough-looking chap standing up on a staith about four feet high holding a great hazel stick and before we got to him he said, 'Aye, another B . . . come to find all't fault he can.'

"Ted Atkinson said, 'You'll not know my friend?'

" 'No, I've never seen, the B . . . before but he'll be another one looking for trouble.'

"So I thought, 'I'll have to be in here.' I said, 'No, I haven't come to find any fault, I'd rather help you.'

"He said, 'I b . . . well know better. I suppose you'll want to look around; I can't stop you. Which way d'you want to go?'

"I said, 'It's your farm, you show me,' and before we got round the place that chap and me were the best of friends, and no-one else could make anything of him. The reason, I found out, was that they'd been going and telling him to do this and that and he was a man who wouldn't bear it. I used to say to him, 'Aye, John, I know you'll try and do so-and-so before I come again,' and he'd say 'I'll try' and that's the way we worked it. They'd been going to kick him off his farm — they had the power — but he was still there when the war ended.

"There was another chap right up at the top of Glaisdale Head, a nice little farm by the roadside, but he was under War Ag supervision and they were talking about shifting him off. He had a good job as an engineer but he'd bought this farm as well. The first time I went to look round there were enough brand new implements to work a 200 acre spot and he only had between 50 and 60 acres. He had a dozen grand Shorthorn cows and I thought 'Whatever's this chap under supervision for?' But his arable land was in a devil of a mess; I could see he'd been trying to plough but didn't know how. He admitted that he didn't know much about it and I said to the Ministry Man, 'You've enough men kicking around at Whitby and Northallerton doing nowt much — you could send one of them up for two or three days to show him how to go on,' and eventually they agreed. It worked, the chap got to use his tractor and his plough and he was away.

"It was no good going with a vicious attitude. If somebody had come here like that I'd have told them to clear off irrespective of what happened. But it's probably true that at the end of the war, and because of the activities of the War Ag, a lot of farms were in better condition than they were at the beginning. There was a lot learned — the man's never been born yet that knows all about farming, or any other trade."

The result of the War Ag's activities was doubling of the crop acreage, a quadrupling of the number of tractors and record harvests when compared with pre-war days.

Everyone had to do some sort of war service, and Leo Welford, at Hinderwell, enrolled in the Royal Observer Corps with a Post on the cliff top. They were kitted out from head to foot in boiler suits. Leo tells the story that, "It was winter time, snow on the ground, and the whole lot of us had coughs and colds. Dr Brash, the Hinderwell doctor, made up a large sweet bottle full of cough mixture and we kept it in the Observer Post. I went in one morning and the bottle was almost empty. I said, 'By gum, they've been giving this socks', and it seemed the lads had been filling their vacuum flasks with it before they went on duty. I said, 'That wants doctoring with something nasty', and my mate Jim Cole said, 'That's given me an idea, I'll fix them', and he doctored it up with Syrup of Figs. I went on duty with a chap one morning. He suddenly ran out and you should have seen him struggling with his overalls in the snow! It was a moving story."

Leo also talked of wartime regulations which affected the movement of animals, and also produced a black market in hams. One of his neighbours was setting off for a feed mill in Bradford to do some dealing and he had a number of hams in the boot of his car when he was stopped.

"What have you got in the boot?"

"It's full of hams," he replied.

"Don't act so daft," was the reply, "we can't be bothered with silly devils like you. Get going" — and off he went!

But he was caught out soon afterwards. The regulation was that you could kill one pig for your own use, and he had killed two; the Ministry Man turned up so he said to his farmhand, "Slip up to the granary and bury one of them pigs under the corn." But his man slipped up — for the inspector spotted that there were two left-side hams in view!

Leo Welford said that hams were fetching four shillings (20p) a pound; his last two weighed 59lbs and 61lbs, "the biggest pig I ever killed". The conversation took place soon after Christmas and went on to prices generally, triggered by recent figures at Ruswarp Mart where "the butchers were bidding for prize tickets to put in their Christmas windows". He claimed that the high prices could not be related to the final cost of the meat, especially after taking into account a 50 per cent loss after killing and another 25 per cent for bone.

In 1944 Mr Welford moved to a larger farm at Scaling; he had been negotiating to buy the Hinderwell farm "and I thought we'd got it but a fellow came along and offered £400 more — the same man had just left the Scaling one that I took over".

When Mr Welford retired his son took over, by which time there were tractors, "but I never used them. I much preferred ploughing with horses. It was a fairly big day doing an acre a day with a pair of horses, in Spring with long days; then you weren't finished — there were the horses to feed and fother up and clean, and much the same next morning. Tractors save a lot of labour but I never liked 'em."

His Shire horse came in very useful three years later in 1947, the year of the Big Snow when the moor road was blocked and the farm was cut off for eight weeks. "They eventually got a milk wagon through to Scaling, at the end of Ridge Lane where we were, and I used the horse and sledge to haul out our milk and that from neighbouring farms. the road blew in every night and was to dig out every morning; the Shire horse didn't like it, he used to jump and buck but we got there. Eventually they got some food as near to us as Calais House and I went with the sledge to collect it, but we needed more and finally we had to go to Loftus for supplies. The snow was as high as the hedges and we walked over the top of them down Grinkle lane to Easington, where a car took us on to Loftus. We didn't lose many sheep because they were mostly indoors but others did and after the snow went there were skeletons galore between Calais House and Scaling Dam."

Much the same story had been told to me by Tom Morley. I had asked him, "Were you cut off in 1947?"

"Cut off, cut off! I remember I went to Whitby in the car one Saturday and had the devil of a job getting back up Sneaton Bank and it was another eight weeks before I got into Whitby again by car.

I went a few times by train from Fyling Hall station, but Dr Beeching put paid to that."

Nelson Hutton, of Sneaton, recalled them cutting out the road down to Ruswarp every day of the week and it was blown in again next morning. "It was an awful job with the small stuff blowing at you in the freezing east wind. We had the iron plough out with a horse but it was a shovel job most of the time. There were a lot of farms badly needing the thresher to get some feed for their animals, and Harry Trenholm managed to get his machine up to us, over fields and anywhere. We had to get our milk as far as Sleights station to get it away to Glaxo at Driffield."

Mr G. Nelson Hutton, born 1918, confirms much of the atmosphere of farming between the wars; he was born at Ugglebarnby which is an extensive hamlet near Sleights just outside Whitby on the Whitby-Pickering road. His grandfather was at Howlett Hall farm nearby and Nelson's father worked for him. In 1926, "about the time of the General Strike, father had thirty bob a week plus some milk and spuds, and that had to keep us — there were five lads and my sister. The land was poor and wouldn't keep a goose to the acre when grandfather rented it in the late 1800s. We used to have to go down a hill and round the back of the church to a spring for drinking water — if you forgot to go at night there was none for breakfast. The rest of the water came from a stream except when they were making butter and for that we had to walk quarter of a mile down fields to a spring for a couple of bucketsfull to wash the butter — it was that cool and fresh."

When the grandparents died Nelson was old enough to work with his father at Howlett Hall for four or five years. He says, "It was a nice enough spot, 92 acres, way out of the road with an old fashioned square yard and buildings all round where you could leave the geese sat on the midden all night with the farmyard doors shut." In 1938 his father moved to Beacon Farm, Sneaton, 162 acres, which he rented for £140 a year and bought in 1947 for £2,900.

"The place was full of rabbits, you could just about walk on them and there was land round the field borders which was eaten on most fields. We didn't get piped water until after the second war, but there were two supplies coming into Sneaton — one came out of our fields and the other was at Pokin Brow which they said would have supplied Whitby if it had been properly looked after and a reservoir built. Nowadays it all comes from the river Esk, and what grand stuff it is! It's soft stuff with chemicals in it, not like the old spring water. It doesn't taste right to me but we'd be badly off without it.

"There was no electricity until 1954; we turned it on for my sister's 21st birthday. We'd had paraffin lamps and then Tilleys. Back at Howlett Hall they had little round holders with a candle stuck in them, you'd wonder how they ever got fothered up and milked, or didn't set fire to the place. My mother used to visit old Seth Burnett and he'd be sat there with a paper in one hand and a candle in't other, and candle grease everywhere. There was an old woman up at Ugglebarnby and when someone called she was reading by candlelight — she said she was saving the electric."

Some of the farming equipment at Hutton's at both Howlett Hall and Sneaton dated back to 1912 when the first binder was bought and it lasted for years until combines came in. North Cave ploughs were made for them by Tom Watson at Sneaton — "he was a good hand at it, he seemed to get the right balance." They used two horses, one in the furrow and the other on the land to be ploughed. "We reckoned to have it all done by Christmas. We had six horses and a young one breaking in; when you were harrowing you oft needed three to a set, another two to drill and for jobs like messing around with a cart. We kept two horses at Sneaton for lang and lang for cutting grass and scruffling up the rows. We had one half-bred Cleveland who was a grand worker but had an awful habit of giving you a sharp nip on the arm if you weren't watching! Originally at Howlett Hall there was a horse wheel in a round house where two experienced horses were yoked with a young one with them

— it was a good spot to break them because they couldn't get out and had no option but to go. Grandad stood in the middle driving them round and round, and it worked a cog on to a round shaft which again worked cogs to turn belts onto pulleys.

"Threshing days were the roughest work; the threshing set usually had the owner and two men with it, and the chap who drove the traction engine. We had to get a load of coal in, and one man would be looking after the fire, one to look after the straw tying and the other was feeding in. We lads were up on top cutting bands and you got the smoke off the chimney stack and the dust off the sheaves, and at night you were all closed up. We hired the equipment from Harry Beeforth at Hawsker or William Rudsdale at Hawsker, but before them there was a chap called Kitson, a queer feller who, if all hadn't been right for him, would maybe knock a gatepost down on the way out.

"There was another mucky job, carrying the chaff and the pulls away and gathering it up for fodder — not like nowadays when it's all blown into a heap and burnt. Not much was burnt in our time, it was a different kind of straw, Sideaway oats were nice fodder. We tied it up in bords or batters with a couple of lengths of Charlie Turner band. After the field was cut you scythed off the baulks round the edges and raked up all that was slathering about. With machines nowadays they aren't tied to leaving a bit lying about. You can look over a hedge and see an armful. Father took the corn to Littlebeck Mill, and in my time to Iburndale Mill and Ruswarp Mill until we got to Sneaton where we had our own machinery."

There was a mill at Ruswarp, it is said, recorded in the Domesday Book and certainly there are records back to the 1600s, but 1989 marks the end of the saga for it has closed and is to be converted into living accommodation.

Back to Nelson Hutton's memories: "The cows liked oat straw, and the corn was used for feed. At one time we used to buy slabs of linseed cake and cotton cake. Barley wasn't reckoned to be good for cattle, it was supposed to give them itchy legs but now they feed barley meal. Turnips were a lot thought of and there was a hand-operated chopper which was hard work until it was eventually connected to an engine — a converted gas engine which went on paraffin. You had to warm it with a blowlamp to get it going, and there was a big flywheel which was a bit dangerous.

"The cows were hand-milked for years, maybe a dozen of them and it wasn't a bad sort of job. Some were a bit hard but while you wanted to get rid of them they were oft the best milkers. All the milk in the early days went into butter, made in a large churn, which Granny Hutton used to take to Whitby market in a pony and trap with a few calls en route." The churn was eventually used for dressing corn. In later years the milk went to Cox's Diary in Whitby and then to Glaxo laboratories at Driffield.

"We used to fatten pigs for bacon and in grandfather's time he used to take three horses and a wagon to Scarborough with a load after a big pig killing. There was a four-year rotation of crops; it was reckoned that every time you ploughed the land over it was worth another bushel an acre when the land was bare fallow . . . It was roots, then barley — undersowed with grass seeds which made the next crop, and then oats. When you were a tenant there was an agreement to sign that you wouldn't sell anything off, manure or straw or anything. It was to make sure you didn't sell off all your hay crop — it had to be eaten on the spot and the manure go back on the land."

When Nelson Hutton's father took over on his own at Howlett Hall in 1933 he made a list of the prices paid for stock:-

Cows: £10 15s, £14 10s, £13. Horses: Bay Mare 20 guineas, Black Mare 22 guineas, Bay 21 guineas, Colt 24 guineas, Filly 27 guineas.

Heifer £12 2s 6d. 11 Pigs at 15s 6d each. 1 Sow £4. 2 Heifers £9 17s 6d each. 1 Bullock £7. 4 Ewes with 8 lambs £2 14s. 1 Calf £3 15. 1 Calf £3 5. 3 Ewes with 6 lambs £2 7s.

1 Calf 10s, 1 Calf £2. 4 Ewes with 4 lambs £1 19s. 1 Calf £2, 1 Calf £1 17s 6d. 5 Ewes with 5 lambs £1 18s. 2 Geld Ewes £1 15s. 5 Gimmers at £1 12s.

Among the Sundries were: 2 Forks @ 2s, Back band 1s 3d, Stretcher 5s, Short traces 2s 6d, Hames 3s and 4s 6d, Collars 11s 6d, 4s, 16s and 14s, Cart saddle £1, Winnowing machine 2s 6d, Pig trough 15s, Scalding tub 5s, Creels 4s, C.T. Harrows 12s 6d, Plough £1 10s, Wheelbarrow 10s, Wagon £5 and another at £1 10s, Dog cart £1 5s, Block carts at £10 and £7 12s 6d, Hay rake £3, Hay turner £7 12s 6d, Grass cutter £4 5s, and Binder £17 10s. 31 Fowls fetched two shillings each.

In wartime the War Ag men came round and said how many acres of corn had to be sown, and which fields to plough out. There was a grant of £2 an acre, "which was all right, it would come in! They'd tell you the thistles wanted cutting, which maybe they did but they upset a few who knew they had plenty to do without that; it was a job with a scythe for a wet day."

"When we sold Beacon in 1983 it fetched £312,000. Father had died aged 85, and I was six months off being on pension. It was a sharing out among the six of us and what with the tax man, the solicitors and accountants, and capital gains tax, by the time they sorted it out — it took three years — we were wondering if we were going to get anything or not."

As for nowadays, there's no encouragement for young people to start, says Nelson Hutton. "They're bulking the farms into bigger units: I could name 20 farms that have disappeared round here in my lifetime — Lumbert Hill, Hag House, Foss Hill and Low Farm at Ugglebarnby; Dean Hall, Lund House, and Monks Farm at Sneaton; Croft Farm at Ruswarp; Longstone, Catwick and Soulsgrave at Sneatonthorpe. Willie Burnett was at the Red Barn at Littlebeck, he had a few cows and was also the postman to outlying farms, but he made a living; now it's split up, and they're building a couple of houses alongside it. Our old Beacon farm is in the process of being sold off apart from 20 acres for a fruit farm.

"I reckon the land's getting ruined with being overfertilised, it must have harmful effects through time. When they're cutting for sileage they're straight in there with the nitrogen and up it comes, green lazy stuff. They reckon the beasts like it but you would think it would get into human systems. There'll be grain mountains as long as they keep paying them for it."

Line up at Castleton ram sale in 1961.

Above: One of the annual traditions is the carrying of a lamb into church — seen here with Jim Winspear at Glaisdale Church, 1957.

Opposite: Jim Richardson, of Newholm, with quadruplet lambs; his ewes were usually producing lambs with the snow thick on the ground.

This page: Henry and Tom Atkinson had a large moor stray on Fylingdales Moor which meant hours of horse riding to gather them for dipping and shearing.

Opposite, top: Henry Atkinson on horseback with a young lamb.

Opposite, bottom: The 150th anniversary dinner of the Blackface Sheepbreeders' Association in October 1970, with (left to right) Jim Muir, Frank Raw, Henry Atkinson and Tom Raw reminiscing.

Inside the clipping shed at Manor House Farm, Goathland, in 1967 with both machine and hand clipping in progress, whilst the fleeces are wrapped in the foreground.

Shearing day at Manor House Farm in 1979 could not have gone ahead without the support of the ladies preparing meals for the hot and hungry men. Mrs. Henry Atkinson is on the left.

A DIARY FOR 1932

A DIARY kept from 1932 onwards gives daily details of activities and the weather (nothing changes!). Judge for yourselves:-

Dec. 16	Windy. Fox hunting and small jobs.
Dec. 17	Very wild. Getting hay in and spreading manure.
Dec. 18	Windy. At Sneaton Church.
Dec. 19	Fine and mild. Bringing straw from Hagg House and turnips, etc.
Dec. 22	Wild. Spreading manure and pulling turnips.
Dec. 24	Fine. At Whitby, poultry cheap. Land dry.
Dec. 25	Very fine. At Sneaton Church twice.
Dec. 28	Fair. Getting hay in and killing pig at Hodgson's.
Dec. 29	Windy and cool. Setting mole traps, sawing sticks.
Dec. 31	Windy and cool. Making hen run. Been a grand open time up to now with the ground dry for time of year, no snow or frost to mention.

1933	
Jan. 9	Very fine. Getting sheep racks and troughs out and starting to feed them, etc.
Jan. 20	Frost and snow. Draining and getting hay in.
Jan. 22	Fine. At Sneaton Church. Skating and teaching Ivy.
Feb. 10	Cold. At H. House ploughing as they all have the flu.
Feb. 26	Mild, ploughing all day.
Feb. 23	Rough day, heavy fall of snow.
Feb. 24	Sneaton lane blocked. Snow plough on road.
Feb. 25	Been a rough night. Lane again full to hedge tops.
Feb. 26	Sleet and rain, thawing but road still blocked. At home all day.
March 4	5 Music lessons unpaid and 6 weeks missed.
March 10	Fair. Got Pony shod, and brushing manure.
March 11	Very fine. Getting hay in. First ewe lambed.
April 11	Getting hay in and tarring lambs, etc. Had one worried in calf garth.
April 25	Some rain, first of a long while. At Hutton's Sale at Howlett Hall.
April 26	Warm. At Store Mart with 8 cattle. Bought cow and 6 stirks. Trade fair for cattle, cows cheap.
May 13	Fine day, wet night. Taking cows and cattle for Featherstone's to Barnby where they are starting farming.
June 1	Turned young calves out.
June 19	Fair. Dipping sheep 35 ewes and 35 lambs. Cooper's Powder Dip.

The delights of living in the country — the road from Lythe to Goldsborough.

A flash flood at Grosmont caught this tractor and trailer in the ford.

June 30   Warm. Making hay up. A lot of grass cut in district, most I have every known in June.
July 10   Showery. Delivering wool.
Aug. 2   Fine. At Military Tournament and hedge switching.
Aug. 12   Warm. Harvest in full swing.
Aug. 20   Fine. Pastures all over brown and bare. A lot of corn led and not much to cut. Land bone dry.
Aug. 23   Odd showers.
Sept. 9   Fine. Threshing. Land still dry and very hard, pastures brown and bare. Turnips look very bad.
Sept. 13   Fine morn, cold wet afternoon. At Barnby Show.
Sept. 24   Wet morn, then fair. First rain of any note for several weeks.
Oct. 18   Dipping sheep, 34 ewes, 1 tup. Little's Fluid Dip.
Oct. 25   Very cold. At Store Mart, lambs more, foals dear, cattle same, cows easy. Led cows and cattle in at nights.
Dec. 5   Nice day, land dry for time of year. Last day out for cattle.
Dec. 23   Cold. Poultry cheap.
Dec. 24   Cold. At home and carol singing.

And so it goes on — On December 31st, 1934, he notes that "cows were out at days till December, grazing well all back end, land now wet and weather mild and wet. Been at Iburndale Mill for grindings and shifting stones, then hare hunting with Beagles at Sneaton from Oxford College. Hares plentiful." Prices noted included one lamb £4 17s 6d, another at £2 17s 6d and one tup at £4 7s 6d, two lambs at 36s = £3 12s, a ewe at £1 14s, and a Scotch ewe at 15s.

At the back of the diary are details of "Collinson's Tup's" activities in 1933:-

Oct. 12   Two of Peirson's ewes but not the rough headed one.
Nov. 5   Dark-faced Wardle ewe, white-faced Parker ewe, Mead's fine-skinned Wensleydale.
Nov. 6   Two eldest Swath ewes, Langdale End ewe, brown-faced leggy Mead ewe.
              "Joseph's Tup" was listed as dealing with, among others:-
Oct. 28   Dark-faced ewe without horns at Woodwarks. Duchess ewe that had 3 lambs, one-eyed ewe and Little Down ewe.

Beasts including a roan cow, a red polled cow and a black heifer were sold to Hutton's, butchers.

On February 28th, 1935, he notes "having first motor driving lesson" and on March 1st he was building a garage.

It is interesting to compare these entries for North Yorkshire with those of South-West Wiltshire as published in a book *Agricultural Records* by J.M. Stratton; he quotes, for 1933, "an exceptionally dry year . . . May warm and dull with many thunderstorms, June warm and sunny. July warm and sunny, except for the north where many thunderstorms, August warm and very sunny, September warm and sunny except in South-East England where much rain fell. Sunshine records were the best of the century (except for 1911). An exceptionally good crop of wheat. Oats above average, also sugar beet. barley about average. hay cut light, and little autumn grass. Wheat 22s 10d per quarter. Establishment of the Milk Marketing Board." The book gives prices back to 1200AD: taking a few years and looking at the price for wheat, and remembering how the value of money has changed, gives:

1626   Wheat 49s 4d per quarter.
1645   51s 3d per quarter.
1659   66 shillings per quarter.
1661   70 shillings per quarter.
1761   30s 3d per quarter.
1861   55s 4d per quarter.
1933   as quoted above — 22s 10d per quarter.
1942   Wartime — 68s 2d per quarter.
1961   89s 8d per quarter.

A quarter of wheat is 4 cwt so multiplying the above prices by about four will give a modern
     equivalent in tonnes. The 1988 average, I am told, is £105 a tonne (£23.62 a quarter)!

HARVEST-TIME AND SHOWS

Harvest-time in September 1958 — from Ravenscar looking across to Robin Hood's Bay.

Harvesting in 1949 at Matthew Stevenson's, Saltwick Bay, near Whitby.

Below and opposite: Matthew Stevenson, aged 80 in 1949. Mr. Stevenson's stacks were thatched and one crowned with a straw fox and the other with a chicken.

Opposite

Top: Threshing day, with Harry Beeforth of Hawsker (foreground) supplying the equipment. January 1958.

Bottom: One stage on from hand-turning the hay — an early hay turner.

This page

Top: Mr. J. E. Raw, secretary of Egton Bridge Old Gooseberry Show for many years, supervising the weighing of berries. The show dates back to 1843.

Bottom: Mr. Tom Ventress's world-beating gooseberry.

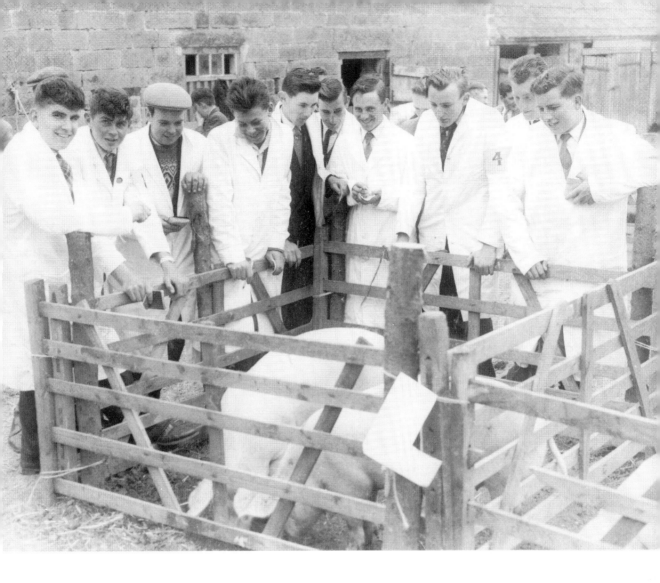

Above: Representatives of Young Farmer's Clubs in Whitby and Castleton area visited Harland's at Newton Mulgrave 1959, and are here assessing the merits of a pig. The number of Y.F.C.'s was probably at its maximum at that time and seems now much less.

Opposite: Jim Muir (and son) of Grosmont, secretary of the Black Face Sheepbreeders' Association, showed off his cattle at Whitby Show in August 1968.

Judging carved walking sticks at Barnby Show in 1958. The head of the stick is usually carved from a sheep's horn.

Who's leading who? — at Egton Show, 1966.

BLACKSMITHS

BLACKSMITHS have featured in story and verse over the years, and possibly have been romanticised as horses became fewer and their work diversified into wrought-iron and fancier work than the daily battles with recalcitrant horses or hooping cart wheels. What has not come out are the "cruel to be kind" manoeuvres that were necessary to get the jobs done, in some instances as the only way to make a horse useable with the other option the knacker's yard. As might be expected a black sense of humour comes out.

All this became apparent in conversation with Eddie Harker, blacksmith — as had been his father — at Mickleby, and who often worked for or with John (America Jack) Welford whose expertise with horses was a legend. Eddie commented that "America was a good man to have with you when a horse was awkward". He recalled one occasion when they went to a pony renowned for kicking; America Jack put his hand under the pony's tail and "gave it a bit of a bend" and there was no more trouble except that after a while it began to tremble.

Jack said, "What's tha trembling at?"

"It's not me, it's the horse," said Eddie.

The lady owner, looking in the door, said, "You're not hurting it, are you?"

"No," said Jack, "I'm just stopping it from wobbling about."

There was another time when Eric Snaith, blacksmith at Danby, was shoeing a Cleveland Bay whilst a publicity film was being made and the horse was not impressed by the occasion. America Jack was there and instructed the cameraman to "keep your shots off its head". He fitted a rope twitch on its nose which he twisted when the horse tried to kick and there was no more trouble. Jack's practical theory was that a horse is bigger and stronger than a man and it was a matter of evening things up.

A horse at Scorton had defeated three smiths when Eddie and Jack were called in; no way would the mare stand for shoeing until Jack tied a rope round its belly, lifted a hind leg through the loop of the rope and let the horse go. She hopped round the field for quarter of an hour and then stood peacefully. "But," said Eddie, "we had to go through the same procedure again before I could shoe the other hind leg."

Jack used much the same idea at Hinderwell Show; a young couple's attempts to groom a pony for the show ring were being defeated by its kicking. Jack lifted a fore leg off the ground and said, "If it kicks now it'll fall ower" — and the trouble immediately stopped. Again, with a stallion at Jack's farm, America House, Eddie arrived and Jack said, "He's not in over good a humour this morning. Watch it." Eddie said that he had hardly started work when "the stallion's head came round, he took hold of the back of my britches and gave me a good shaking. Jack shouted at him and he dropped me. So Jack tied a leg up and we went in for breakfast; half an hour later and the horse was as good as gold."

Obviously, then, Jack had a way with horses. A commonly held opinion is that his farm was "run on kicking horses" sent by their owners as a last resort. If Jack couldn't cure them, the knacker's yard was the alternative. Obviously, too, he was a useful man to the blacksmiths of the area and generally knowledgeable — except in one instance. When Jack's father was alive the farmyard had dozens of brown Runner Ducks "which", Jack commented, "got into the house and skittered all over the place." So much so that when his father died Jack got rid of the ducks.

In the next two years four horses died, and when a fifth fell ill the vet was called in (an expensive exercise to be avoided as long as possible). He said, "Where are the ducks?"

"Gone and good riddance," said Jack.

"You'd better get some back," said the vet and explained that the ducks ate the worms which inhabited the open water troughs around the yard from which the horses drank, and these worms were the cause of the fatalities.

The cost of calling out the vet or the blacksmith was discussed long and hard in pre-war days. "Times were very hard when my father was a smith," said Eddie Harker, "Farmers used to pay their bills in corn and straw, a few bags of oats, or turnips. We had some stock and dad used it on his smallholding. That way we all survived."

Opposite: Eddie Harker shaping a shoe at Mickleby smithy.

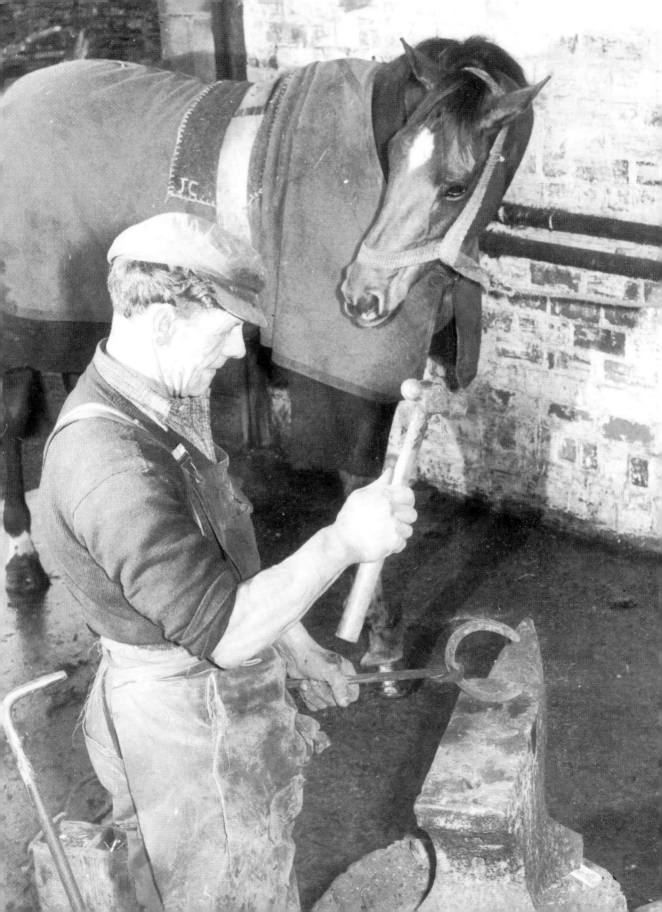

Above: Jim Severs, blacksmith at Roxby forge, with America Jack holding his mare. John Welford jnr. holds a Cleveland Bay. The plaque over the forge dated 1858 "Turton Cottages" marks the owners of many of the farms in the area.

Opposite: America Jack's mare is shoed by Jim Severs.

Above: Mr. A. Dowson, and his son Arthur at Egton smithy; they also worked in wrought-iron and made massive ornamental gates for Low Stakesby Manor, Whitby. March 1958.

Opposite: Jack Cook — and his father before him — had his smithy in lower Church Street, Whitby. About 1930 he was confronted with a very unusual job — to shoe thirty oxen. The Atora Suet Company, for publicity, organised a train of fifteen covered wagons, each drawn by two oxen, to tour the country. They had been fitted with leather shoes which had worn and Jack was asked if he could shoe them. The first job was to hand-make nails to fix the shoes and then, over the course of a week, he fitted the whole herd.

Tom Watson, of Sneaton smithy, at work making a North Cave plough shaft.

The smithy at Lythe, on the green just outside the gates of Mulgrave Castle, home of the Normanby family, has its own tradition; special occasions are marked by the Firing of the Stiddy. The anvil is taken outside, upturned, and a hole in the base packed with gunpowder which is touched off by a long rod heated in the smithy fire, shooting a wooden plug into the air with a resounding crack. This occasion was the birth of Lord Normanby's heir, the Earl of Mulgrave, in February 1954.,

CLEVELAND BAYS

A GREEN and pleasant land — with the emphasis on the green? The fumes from the tractors add to the atmospheric pollution and the artificial fertiliser kills off the fish in the streams. The Greenhouse Effect is added to, according to a book *The End of Nature* by Bill McKibben, by flatulent cattle, not to mention horses, pigs, sheep and goats, to the extent of 73 million tonnes of methane gas a year, an increase of 435 per cent since last century. He warns of the "terrible threat posed to the ozone layer by herds of those velvet-eyed innocent chewers of cud whose fermenting gastric bacteria give off vast quantities of methane gas". The hens in their batteries are suspected of salmonella and the hormones in meat endanger generations to come. And as for knocking down hedges to make larger fields to help to increase production, the National Park are handing out thousands of shrubs and trees to re-populate the landscape. The corn that was rejected because it wouldn't produce flour whiter than white now produces a crop that brings a higher price, and using nothing but cowhouse muck puts up the price of the cabbages. The old farmers must be laughing up their sleeves at what has been heralded as progress — with a wry smile at modern farmers being paid to keep fields fallow.

A ride on a flat farmcart behind an old mare is advertised as a country attraction, and farmers possessing a pair of horses and a plough, offering a look around the pigstyes and a play with the lambs, attract thousands to pay for a day in the country. Next thing they'll be advertising Muck Spreading Days — bring your own green wellies and fork!

Certainly the horse has come back into his own — a long way from the war years and after when the need for production to negate the activities of Hitler's submarines, and the post-war need for food, meant more and more acres in production and the tractor was king. Hundreds of cart horses went for slaughter; feed was short and those that were kept were seldom worked and went soft and unfit for any kind of work. When the tide first began to turn in the 1960s, when hunting came to the fore and pony clubs blossomed, the horses were not there to be bought. Some breeds had disappeared entirely and the Cleveland Bay, native to the northern moors, was down to about thirty mares and seven stallions nationwide. The only saving grace was that they included three sire lines and eight female lines and could be the base for building up stock.

The history of this ancient breed is well documented, back to the days when it was known as the Chapman horse after its use by the Chapmen who carried goods for sale from village to village across the moors with a string of Cleveland Bays as pack horses. George Stephenson's railways eventually eliminated the trade but even those carriages in the early days were drawn along the rails by Clevelands on inclines too steep for the primitive steam engines.

The Cleveland Bay Horse Society had a policy of only breeding pure Clevelands but to meet the demands of the new market for even-tempered heavy weight hunters the policy was altered. The change was vitally necessary for such was the shortage of mares in 1962 that would-be C.B. purchasers were advised to use a C.B. stallion on their own mares — long-standing members of the

Society had strongly resisted any change in policy but this alteration was allowed because no dilution of the blood line was involved.

A new problem arose because the remaining mares were fat and hadn't bred for years. It took a hard winter in 1962 to slim them down and in 1963 many were in foal. As one stallion owner put it, there was a lot of unladylike squealing but it happened! A change from pre-war was that mares were generally brought to the farm where the stallion was standing instead of him travelling an area with his stallion man. As far back as the 1800s owners of stallions advertised and printed notices giving the places where the horse would stand for part of a day; the C.B. Society decided which stallion went into an area, taking into account blood lines already there and a stallion might well be imported from another part of the country. Immediately post-war, America Jack Welford travelled a stallion "Apollo" for three or four days a week; seven or eight mares might be served in a day with three or four foals resulting.

Pre-war there had been a small export market, particularly to Japan, and after the war the demand returned but it was only after several years that the Society deemed it wise to let any leave this country. Prices had risen: a comparison has been given for 1943 when a Cleveland Bay cost £143, the same price as an Austin Seven car. Since then the prices have had much the same relationship, "but", being Yorkshire, "it's very much what you can get," I was told.

The worth of the Cleveland line is shown by its popularity in royal circles where, surely, their choice is as infinite as the breeds available. In this century King George V had 26 horses and mares and more recently a stock has been maintained in the Royal Mews as coach horses, the pick of which have been used by the Duke of Edinburgh in coaching competitions. Success in show jumping was shown by "North Flight", a Cleveland/Thoroughbred cross which took part in the Tokyo Olympics and Harvey Smith's "Madison Time" in the Mexico Olympics. "Rembrandt", "Viscount" and "Island Monarch", among others, have won national three-day events.

Still you will find farmers who keep them for their mundane qualities — tidy feet that walk neatly between rows for scruffling and the like. Tractors and the heavy implements that they draw, while infinitely faster, do compress the land and work can be held up for long periods in wet weather. The horse is much slower but can be used when the tractor stays in its shed. The horse reproduces itself, provides valuable organic fertiliser and consumes forage grown on the farm. The tractor does none of these things.

"Perhaps," say the old farmers, "one day the oil will run out and the horse will come back into its own."

In March 1967, when the desperate post-war shortage of Cleveland Bays had been partly overcome, this colt was freed for export to Italy. Holding it is George Nelson, horseman to Miss Ruth Kitching, secretary of the Cleveland Bay Society, at Fryup Gill, Danby.

Above: Inside the stables at the Royal Mews, Buckingham Palace, with Miss Ruth Kitching and America Jack Welford discussing Cleveland Bays with the Royal Equerry, Col. Sir John Miller. May 1965.

Opposite, top: Cleveland Bay crosses are used in the royal coaches and these were pictured in the Mews for a publicity film for the Cleveland Bay Society in 1965.

Opposite, bottom: 13 July 1965 — the year when Cleveland Bays were featured at the Great Yorkshire Show. The Queen sent royal coaches, staff and some of the Cleveland Bay crosses from the Royal Mews for a ceremonial parade.

A meet of the Glaisdale Harriers included six riders on pure Clevelands or first crosses at Fryup Hall, home of Miss Ruth Kitching. 1967.

Cleveland Bay mares and foals at Fryup Gill, 1964.

TALES OF COUNTRY FOLK

WHILE making tape recordings over the past twenty-five years I have enjoyed listening to many anecdotes from country folk, some obviously true, some tongue in cheek, some embroidered from overheard conversations in the local pub — and containing conjecture solidified into fact with the passing years. Others were definitely manufactured to entertain! I leave it to the reader to sort out which from which.

Bill Weatherill was the postman at Lealholm for thirty years, walking twenty miles a day − "kept you in fair good fettle, like, you weren't carrying a lot of extra weight".

"There was always something happening; I remember when the last war started and Danby Beacon was opened up as an RAF station, and the lads were lodging around the villages. One of them was staying with us and fancied coming on my walk over to Shortwaite. I left a letter at one farm and went on further down and when we came away back t'auld lady was down at the roadside on her knees with some paper and a pen. I stopped and said, 'Now what's up?'

" 'Why,' she says, 'you've fetched me a letter and they want an answer to it and I want you to write for me.'

" 'Tell what you want to say,' I said, 'and I'll put it down for you,' and I did and the airman was ivver si capped. he said, 'I never thought you'd have things like that to do.' But it was regular, and because for her and many an outlying farm the nearest letter box was miles away, I regularly brought back about as much mail and parcels as I'd set off with.

"There was a time," said Bill, "when the Post Office were wanting folks to get the telephone in and they put slogans on envelopes when they were cancelling the stamps. I'd delivered a letter to an old fellow who lived in a cottage on the moor end; when he'd lifted it up off the floor and had a look at it, it was addressed to him alright, like, but right across the top it said, 'You are wanted on the Phone.' He was clean upset about it, and he got himself done up and off down to Lealholm and went into the Post Office and swailed it through the window at the Postmaster, 'That isn't for me, that isn't mine.'

"The Postmaster read it and said, 'Of course it's for you, there's your name and address.'

" 'How the hell can it be for me" Can't you see what it says on it — You are wanted on the phone — I've never been on't b . . . phone in me life.' "

Bill Weatherill was also renowned for his Yorkshire dialect readings, a hobby he had in common with the late Mr F. Austin Hyde, headmaster of Lady Lumley's Grammar School at Pickering; the latter also wrote much original material and the following was a favourite item of Bill's:

Dapper, Auld Mare

by F. Austin Hyde

Have I any old hosses Young feller from Hull?
You're willing to buy 'em, give value in full.
Why yes, I hae yan in't paddock down here
Come up, then, come on then, Dapper auld mare.

Nae, she doesn't come galloping but then, you see
T'mare's a bit wankled like, gone twenty three.
You'll mebbe not be quite so frisky thissen
When tha's seen thi great grandsons grow up to be men.

What will I take for her? Well, now, she's fat
And they tell me you give a bit extra for that;
But I might as well tell tha thou'll not by that mare
If tha stands there and bids me from now to next year.

She was fost foal I had when we come up on't place
And first she's been allus in shaft, pole or trace;
She's plewed, drilled and harrowed, rolled, scruffled and led
And mothered Beaut, Boxer, Prince, Bobby and Ned.

If t threshing machine got stuck fast on its way
Young hosses would plunge, rive and tew half a day,
But afore it got shifted it always was 'Here,
Away thew garns, Storry, and fetch us t'auld mare.'

When t's stacks was afire before motor car days
She galloped ti Driffield when't spot was ablaze,
Ovver fields, ditch and hedgerow fer't gainest way round
And saved buildings and t'house and three lives I'll be bound.

When't missus took badly when't babby was born
T'was a life and death journey for't Doctor that morn;
And though she'd been working at t'pleaf all day long
Mare galloped as though she knew summat was wrong.

Wi' never a whip nor a jerk on the reins
She went like a whirlwind and flew back again
Wi't Doctor and Nurse just in time to save life.
Auld Dapper, I owe thee both daughter and wife.

On friends that's si faithful we deant turn our backs,
Nor send them for slaughter to't foreigner's axe.
Nor let 'em be worked to their death across't sea
Where nivver a Yorkshire voice says Woe, or Gee.

No, now that's she's neither young, bonny nor sound
She owns lahtle paddock, it's Pensioners' Ground,
And stall in yon stable, hay, bedding and corn
I reckon she's addled a spot of her own.

And when the day comes that we do have to part
She'll gan in a way that'll not break her heart
And t'land that she's worked on and loved twenty year
At last'll lig light on me faithful auld mare.

****

Many readers will have fond memories of Major John Fairfax Blakeborough, born in Guisborough in 1883 and who lived for many years until his death at Westerdale, Castleton. Fond memories arise particularly in the area covered by the old style *Whitby Gazette,* of his weekly column started in 1902 of the doings of Lizzie Leckonby, Mary Thompson and Mattie Pearson which nowadays are much used in Yorkshire dialect readings. But that was a very small part of his output which added up to 108 books, mostly on the history of racing; he had been an owner, trainer and a well respected judge at racecourses around the country. Originally a Teesside journalist, he became a freelance before the 1st World War; he joined up on the second day "if I can have a horse", and was posted to the Hussars where he was awarded the Military Cross. After the 2nd War, when horses were rapidly being replaced and the Cleveland Bay breed was down to three or four stallions in the whole country, he was one of those instrumental in rescuing the breed. He was secretary for many years, later president and finally life governor of the Cleveland Bay Society.

His October column in the *Whitby Gazette* inevitably included, "Christmas follows closely on the tail of the last horse in the St. Leger." Other bon mots attributed to him included, "People in Cleveland are never old until they reach 100 — and then they can say they're getting on a bit."

He reminisced about the Vessel Cup Singers (Wassail Cup), Dora Palmer and Mizza Cole, who used to tour Whitby and district in the weeks before Christmas. "They started," said he, "the last fortnight in October so they got all their calls in before Christmas; they each carried a little cardboard box in which was a doll and various oddments including an orange. Whatever you did when they called, you must never show amusement. They sang their own version of 'God Rest Ye, Merry Gentlemen' whilst you crossed their palms with silver — and there was definitely a feeling of the Evil Eye if you didn't!"

It was at a celebration party for Fairfax's 90th birthday that the following tale was told:-

Henry had been working for one firm all his life and he felt he was fit and hale and hearty. He liked his pipe of bacca and, at 65, he reckoned he could go on working for a few years yet but he was called into the office and the gaffer said, "Thank you very much for your long and devoted service, you can go and keep your wife company now", or words to that effect, which took Henry somewhat aback; he reckoned he was nowt but a lad.

Major J. Fairfax Blakeborough.

He went home and Martha, seeing his woebegone expression, said "Whatever's up, lad?'

"They've sacked me," he said, "there's no pay off and the government's pension won't even buy ale and bacca."

"Hang on a minute," said Martha, "come over here with me.": She took him into the front parlour and pointed out of the window: "You see those three cottages over there next to the pub? Well, lad, they're all ours."

Henry looked at her as if she was fond: "Deant be si daft, how can they be ours?"

"They are ours, Henry, bought and paid for, and I'll tell you how it's come about. When we got wed I thought every time you made love ti me I'd put half a crown away and after t'fost year I had eneaf ti buy t'fost cottage. After another ten years I bought the second one and now, Henry, when we've been married forty years I've just managed to buy the third 'un."

Henry was completely taken aback. He looked sideways at her: "Why ivver didn't you tell me? If ah'd known I wouldn't have played around si mich and we'd have had t'pub at the end as well."

****

Arthur Mennell was the village joiner, undertaker and stockist of tools and equipment plus bits needed by local households at Robin Hood's Bay — as his father had been before him. The workshop was on the top side of Fylingthorpe, shelved all around and each shelf full of items wrapped in tissue paper — hand-painted Victorian pot door knobs and the like which twenty years later, after Arthur's time, were high fashion. When the workshop was cleared into Gray's Saleroom after his death they fetched prices that would have amazed him. I bought my first portable tape recorder in 1962 and his was the first voice I recorded: he was suspicious of the recording machine but decided to ignore it and continue as normal with his vivid storytelling. He did not, however, indulge in his well remembered ability to recite Classics and long sections of Shakespeare from memory.

He was eighty years old and he was talking about his apprentice days. He related that there was a lady, Mrs Dixon, who lived until she was ninety-nine and three quarters, and she was a customer. "When she got a start cleaning she needed a pound of drab paint but she always brought a two-pound earthenware jar that Altham's jam used to be in, so she 'could get her finger in't top to carry it down'. It was over dark or over light for her; she'd paid for a pound which was sixpence then, and by the time I'd finished doctoring to her satisfaction she'd got two pounds, 'enough to do t' window stones and the kitchen table frame and legs'. Then, the blind in her kitchen took a yard and a half of blind cord, but that really wasn't long enough; those old fashioned ones had a drag pulley to pull up and you had to stitch the cord on, not knot it. It was a penny a yard, which made three halfpence, but she said, 'If you measures it slack as it comes out of the box I'll do the stretching', and she used to stretch it out on the iron railings in front of her house for a week and it did it.

"So far that totalled sevenpence halfpenny. Then, the stairs up into her attic were dog-leg, winders, 'and sometimes', she said 'I have to double the carpet twice or three times. I want a pennorth of tacks — give me middling and long 'uns; when you buy them penny boxes they aren't full.' I said they're not supposed to be. She said, 'I've nowt to put 'em in so I've brought a half stone flour bag', and she kept saying she'd better have a few more long 'uns and made sure she'd got her money's worth. That made eightpence halfpenny — which was put on an account."

It was Arthur's switching from the factual to the unbelievable that entertained me as it had done in Robin Hood's Bays hostelries for many years: "It was at Robin Hood's Bay old churchyard at the top of the bank," he continued, "and there was a grave to dig. At the low end of it there's an anchor and a very elaborate stone and beyond it was an uncharted bit of ground because it was a bit awkward. There'd been a man buried there, a vagrant who'd been working at Swalhead Quarry and got killed in a rock fall, and he was buried by the Poor Law, not a posh outfit and it was forgotten and not recorded. It was a lovely sunny morning when the gravedigger started and he was well on the way by ten o'clock when he knocked off for a pint up at the Raby Castle pub in Raw village. When he came back and started again with his spade it was hollow. Then he struck something hard and it turned out to be a wood plank; he split it across and up popped a pair of clogs.

" 'Damn it,' he said, 'this isn't uncharted ground.' He went to the other end and worked more reverently, and as he raised the lid end the feller popped up and said, 'Is it Resurrection Day?'

" 'No,' said the gravedigger, 'we're a bit early for the Resurrection.'

" 'Why are you disturbing me?'

The gravedigger explained that he was getting ready to put another one in alongside him.

" 'Did I give you a bit of a shock?'

" 'Aye,' said the gravedigger, 'if I hadn't had a couple of pints . . .'

" 'How much is beer a pint now?'

" 'A shilling,' said the gravedigger.

" 'To hell with that. It was twopence halfpenny when they popped me in here. Put the lid on again.' "

"There was another tale," said Arthur, "of that old churchyard. There was an old tramp walking from Scarborough Strand to Whitby Poorlaw, and he was going up that hill and not having a watch he had a look at the sundial on the church and saw it was about half past eleven. He knew he couldn't get into the Whitby Union Workhouse until five o'clock so he had a bit of time to put in. He sat down near the porch and nearby was an old headstone with a ship on; the epitaph read:

> *Sons of the Ocean, read this tombstone o'er*
> *Brother Harrison has but gone before.*
> *All you young, ye rich, ye proud*
> *You all must die and wear a shroud*
> *So be prepared to follow me.*

The old tramp read it over and thought a minute; there was a lot of dead grass over the base of the stone, and quite a bit of stone vacant so he found a bit of soft stone and he wrote:

> *To follow you I'm not content*
> *Until I know which way you went."*

The cottage next to Arthur's workshop in Thorpe was at one time occupied by an old gamekeeper before it was altered and "he was a very conscientious sort of a chap," said Arthur. "He could be awkward, he'd been a gamekeeper where at times he had 'to be as fierce as a blind pig'. But when I knew him he was a bit slow in movement with age, and bent with the two 'W's' — work and worry — and it was about March. I was in this paint shop mixing some stuff and he wandered round the garden; it took him a long time to get on here.

" 'Now Arthur,' he said, 'It's a grand day.'

" 'Aye,' I said, 'it's a lovely day.'

" 'Why,' he says, 'I'm, thinking about tackling the garden but she gets bigger each year. I want to buy a potato fork if you has one, a digging fork.'

'Yes,' I replied, 'Two half dozens only came in this last week; I'll cut the string and then you can select one.'

"And he looked at it. Now these garden forks were painted just where they go into the shaft in red. He said, 'I nivver liked paint on a thing. When I was a lad there was a farm sale, they used to paint both the wheelbarrow, cart and wagon up and when you got it home it mebbe dropped to bits.'

"I commented, 'You make a selection and I'll go on with me mixing.'

"Presently he came back and said, 'I think I'll take this one. How much is it?' I answered, 'Ten bob,' and now they're twenty-one and sixpence.

"So he went down the garden with it. I was looking out of the window about half an hour later and he came up with the handle in one hand and the tines in the other. He waddled away round. I let him speak first. He said, 'It's come to grief.'

" 'Yes,' I said, 'It's disintegrated.'

"He said, 'I warn't rough with it.'

"I replied, 'I know you wouldn't be rough with it.' He was never rough with anything in his life where work was concerned.

"He said, 'What are we going to do?'

"I replied, 'They're all there, make another selection.'

" 'Aye,' he said, 'but how does tha' know next 'un won't be the same as this one, disintegrate tha called it?' He went on, 'The only thing I can account for is that I must have left a biggish tatey in the ground at the back end and struck it.' "

Arthur had gone into the family business when he was fourteen years old and one of his first jobs, he said, was down at the bottom of Robin Hood's Bay bank. "Some of those houses next to the cliff, the sea air played bob duck with the door locks; there was an old fisherman, he'd lost his wife, he used to take a middlin drop of drink, and on his door — a batten door facing the sea — there'd been three locks already when I was sent for to fit another one, and none of the keyholes had been plugged up. So I said, 'Should I plug these keyholes up?'

" 'Oh no,' he said, 'It makes it confusing if anybody tries to break in.'

" 'All right,' I said, 'I'll leave it', and I made another keyhole, which meant there were four keyholes but only one with a lock on.

"However, that was not the end of the matter," said Arthur. "One night he was in the Mariners' Tavern, and he got a drop over much ale and said, 'I took't key out of me pocket, shoved it into't hole and the lock wasn't there. It went in't floor and I had to sleep in the Gas House till morning.'

(The 'Gas House' was Robin Hood's Bay Gas Works up a yard at the bottom of the old village where coal gas was manufactured and which by means of a tiny two-stroke paraffin engine supplied the village. The one advantage was the warmth; the disadvantage the smell of burnt coke!)

"Then," continued Arthur Mennell, "he would have these spare holes plugged up but he said, 'Don't bring any bits of wood, I have plenty of beer bottle corks', and we stuffed them in instead."

Arthur Mennell had a grandfather who was a farmer near Hackness who used to tell this moralistic tale of a neighbour:-

"He was opening a field out for harvest, cutting the baulks round the side with a scythe. Whilst he was working a clergyman was walking past — he'd been a curate and just got appointed to the local church — and he had two maiden sisters with him.

" 'Hello,' he said, 'there's a man here preparing for harvest.' He tapped on the gate with his stick but the farmer was busy.

"One of the maiden sisters remarked, 'Aren't country folks ignorant! He's either deaf or daft or both. He can't even stand up straight.'

"At this the farmer straightened his back and walked slowly over. He said, 'I've heard all your remarks. Now look, this is a fine field of corn, a good crop. You'll notice that full heads hang down and empty ones stand straight up.' "

****

One thing I have envied in country folk is the ability to have the right answer ready at the crucial moment; think not that country minds are slow — there may be a short period of quiet contemplation but when the answer comes it hits home. Not even a starched hospital sister could beat this one . . .

Bill Hodgson retired from farming at Dunsley to a cottage in Sandsend and, at 70 years old, needed to go into hospital for a hip operation; what worried his family — and this story comes from his son — was not so much the operation as the fact that he smoked black twist tobacco in his pipe.

"You'll be allowed to smoke sometimes," they told him, "but you'll poison the rest of them if you smoke that stuff", so they bought an ounce of ready-rubbed tobacco of a lighter variety.

He went into Scarborough hospital. The time came for a smoke but, being a twist man where you carve a few flakes off the block, rub it between your hands, gently tamp it down into the pipe and then, and only then, possibly twenty minutes later, strike a contemplative match, a loving procedure which gives time for reflection, he naturally began to treat what they'd given him in similar fashion. He was lying back in bed, gently rubbing the ready-rubbed between his somewhat horny hands with bits dropping on the counterpane and on the floor, when Sister walked in. "Mr Hodgson, what are you doing? What's all that mess?" she enquired.

"Nay, missus," said he, "them's mouse droppings. T'mattress is full of the little devils."

****

I was invited to attend the "Ceremony of the Ribbons" at the pub at Goldsborough some years ago, with no immediate explanation of what it was; it might have been Druids or a meeting of an Ancient Order of Shepherds but turned out to be a three hundred years old custom which used to be observed all over the north; however the evening began in a prosaic way with a domino drive. The winner, Tom Gallon, a farmer from Ugthorpe, having been presented with his prize of a pair of braces (gallasses), was required to sing and the words were unusual:-

> *The Bride's good health we now will sing*
> *In spite of the Turk and the Spanish King.*
> *The Groom's good health we'll not let pass,*
> *We'll have them both into one glass.*
>
> *See, see, see that he drinks it all,*
> *See, see, see that he lets none fall*
> *For if he do, he shall have two*
> *And so shall the rest of the Company round.*

Tom Blair, of Handale Abbey farm near Loftus, invented a cutter for drainage trenches in 1950.

The second and third prizes were socks and a tie, all of which had been provided by the last couple to be married from the village.

Which aroused my interest: to my knowledge we were never fighting the Turks and the Spaniards at the same time — so the words of the song apparently didn't fit the facts. But some research sorted it out: "Turk" in the 17th century was a common appellation for pirates, so the reference was to a sailor getting safely home through the Mediterranean and the Bay of Biscay for his wedding.

Secondly, the "Ceremony of the Ribbons" goes back to that time; originally it was not to do with ribbons but the bride's garter which she made as a sample of her needlework and wore on her wedding day. After the ceremony the garter was a prize for a race on horseback by the lads of the village, from the church to the bride's home. But the lads were impatient, and one sneaked into church as the bride knelt at the altar and slipped off the garter so they could get on with the race! That was too much. The prize changed to a bunch of ribbons. The horse race became a running race — which, because there were complaints of outsiders coming in and winning, was changed to a domino competition, which is where I came in.

There is a tailpiece to the story; should the couple not provide the prizes there is a procession to their home after closing time, and a white chamber pot is smashed on their doorstep. Far fetched? No, that did happen not so long ago.

Country weddings were a frequent occurrence when the author was a photographer and, whilst some incidents are better left unrecorded, one or two stay in vivid memory. Some thirty years ago a couple married in the district and the bride's brother, George, was a groomsman who was not to be found when the group pictures were to be taken. "He's had to go back," someone said, "one of the cows is calving."

One of the bystanders said to the bride, "Nivver mind lass, it might have been you" — at which point she burst into tears and fled back into church, from whence it took half an hour of pleading by her mother, by the vicar and her new husband before she would agree to come out.

There was also the story of the lost bridegroom; the guests, the groomsmen, the bridesmaids and finally the bride in all her splendour turned up at church. Time passed but no sign of the groom. Fears were expressed that he had done a runner but a search was organised and an hour later he was run to earth.

Most farms have an area in front of the house loosely known as a garden which the farmer doesn't wish to recognise as his responsibility and his wife thinks it is, with the result that it tends to be an overgrown wilderness. Here was found the missing groom, fast asleep in a deck chair. As they said, "Of all the daft places to go — nobody ever goes in there."

The last — and most recent — brush with the farming fraternity will stay in memory for a very long time . . .

In 1983 Hummersea Farm, near Skinningrove, was up for sale and the agents commissioned the author to photograph the outbuildings and the farmhouse to illustrate the sale brochure; accompanied by his young lady assistant, who had started work the previous week and knew little of country folk, they arrived and introduced themselves to the incumbent. The outbuildings were soon dealt with, and, coming up to midday, the farmer pointed out that the best view of the house was through the front garden and up a steepish slope into a hen run, and said he was going in for his dinner.

So the author led the way with assistant at his heels through the garden and, entering the hen run, there was a wire across the ground at ankle level over which he tripped. There was a loud explosion at close quarters, the farmer came out and said, "I forgot to tell you — someone's been thieving my chickens so I fixed a trip wire to a shotgun," and proceeded to re-load it!

Mr. George Coverdale (mounted, centre) celebrated his 80th birthday with a special meet of the Glaisdale Hunt at his home, Danby Castle.

Lady Maria Lewes walking the Goathland Hounds near the kennels on Eskdaleside. May 1965.

John Pyman MFH with the Goathland Hounds, 1953.

Winner of the hunting horn contest at Glaisdale Gymkhana in 1958.

Above: Lord and Lady Normanby with the Goathland Hunt at Mulgrave Castle. December 23rd, 1978.

Opposite, top: The Glaisdale Harriers maintain the annual tradition of the opening meet at Ainthorpe where a hare stew is served. This was the scene in 1954. But they have hunted the fox for many years.

Opposite, bottom: 84-year old hunt follower John Marwood (centre) with, among others, George Puckrin, hunt secretary, John Pyman M.F.H., Bill Cornforth and Fred Booth.

"Squire" Jim Winspear, a Master of the Glaisdale Hunt and very well known character in the farming world, takes a break from raking hay.

EPILOGUE BY A MODERN FARMER

IT'S a moving story — it probably began in the formative years of the earth when continents were splitting apart, the ice was melting at the end of the Ice Age and the sea filled in the gaps between landmasses and the temperature changed. Men, what few there were, migrated to areas where life was more pleasant — and the animals also moved. The cultivated areas we now have are nothing to do with where they started, the Sahara was once a green and pleasant land — and the current droughts in Africa and in central U.S.A. may or may not be a new pattern of change. There is a contention that the pattern in America has been changing for some time, not so much by nature but by a realisation that poorer growing areas should be let go, and cultivation concentrated in the better areas — but that doesn't take into account how that policy may have to change if the drought in the Prairies continues in years to come.

What does the future hold? Is there a world food-shortage or is there, as it would seem to me, an insoluble problem of the wrong crops being grown in the wrong places? And will the weather — whether or not distorted by the "Greenhouse Effect" or other man-produced cataclysms — have the final say?

"Whatever the changes two factors must always be borne in mind," says Sir Michael Shaw, M.P., "firstly the land remains with us. It is an asset that we must make the best use of, whatever the changes may be. Above all, we must never forget those who work on the land, often for generations. As their families have adapted their way of life to the changing needs of the countryside in the past, so they must be given the opportunity to adapt again in keeping with their own well-being and the future use of the land they have always lived and worked on."

Martin Burtt is a hill farmer with 200 acres at Glaisdale Head, all grass, and running dairy cows and sheep. Not only that but he appears on farming programmes on T.V., is a member of the NFU Council and has been over to Brussels on numerous occasions, is Vice Chairman of the NFU Less Favoured Areas Committee, a Council member of the North Yorkshire Moors Association, County Chairman (in 1981) for the NFU in the North Riding and Durham and is young enough to have years of farming ahead of him.

As might be expected, he has strong views; ask him about the number of farmers leaving the land and the blame is not placed where you might expect. "The banks are sympathetic, the E.E.C. tries to be helpful," he says, "but there's a growing trend for yuppies from the south, where there's been a money explosion, to sell up down there and buy farm buildings up here with an acre or two for the pony, and still have change in their pockets. That is forcing farming and country people out who want to live and work in the village where they grew up, it's pushing up prices so that young people who want to come into farming are held up by the vast amount of capital needed. Do they expect a yuppie bank manager from down south to maintain dry stone walls?"

Obviously a very sore point, and he is also critical of the way that the accomplishments of farmers in wartime and the post war period, when production was encouraged and increased five-fold to

Martin Burtt of York House Farm, Glaisdale.

feed the population, are ignored; that the sacrifice of three-quarters of the labour force has been made in a major slimming operation; that the remaining farmers are expected to become more environmentalists and conservationists than farmers.

"There's been a continuing cutback in the number of farms and holdings in the North York Moors. Farming is going through what the steel, coal, car and shipbuilding industries have gone through in the last ten years. There have been a few farmers who have not been prepared to change, have fallen foul of the economic climate, and had to sell up; the signs have been there long enough for them to see. There is some government money coming into farming in the form of the H.L.C.A. — Hill Land Compensatory Allowance — which is a hill cow and sheep subsidy to the tune of £120 million throughout the UK and Wales which at first sight might seem an awful lot of money. But I assure you that to hill farmers it is as essential as petrol is to a car; in fact in many cases the amount they receive is the sum total of their farm profits, that's what they live on, they're totally reliant on it, they can't survive without it."

The reader might be gaining the impression that Mr Burtt is an arm-chair critic — and could not be more mistaken; he is very much a working farmer. His dairy herd was affected, like every other farmer, by the imposition of milk quotas. "It hurt me like everyone else at the beginning because there was a direct cut in the milk I could sell and therefore it hit my income. But since then we've had a value attached to the quota because we've created a commodity. Like all commodities it attracts a value and that has been a help, it puts a bottom on the market and the introduction of quotas has not done dairy farmers any harm in the long term. It has made us all look inwardly to see whether we are efficient or not and cut out ways we've been gettin away with for years. We're a slimmer, more efficient business now."

I asked him how many of his dairy herd he had to cut out.

"We didn't: we went about it another way and cut our inputs. The biggest cost is dairy cake and we cut back from two tons per cow per year to 30 cwts and now to 25 cwts and that has made all the difference. The cows ate more sileage as a consequence. Believe it or not, the milk production didn't go down as dramatically as I expected, the cows didn't lose their condition or their fertility, and there was no trouble getting them back in calf."

"It is obvious," said Mr Burtt, "that in years past we have been conned into feeding far more concentrates than was necessary — 'more cake — meant more milk — meant more profit' we were told and we went along with it. Now those of us who stayed in milk are learning to live with quotas and are realising that there is far more profit to be gained from feeding lots of well made sileage and getting much more production is possible from that sileage."

A document from the Ministry of Agriculture had suggested that there should be a cut-back on artificial fertilisers, and reference back to an earlier chapter shows that Mr Tom Morley was puzzled by the size of the cheque he had written and the fact that they were still spreading as much muck as they ever did. But for Mr Burtt cutting back on cake meant the cows ate more sileage — an increase from 7 to 8 tons per cow per year to 9 to 10 tons — and therefore more grass was needed.

"We still put muck on the land, it puts the nature back and if the land loses its humus you have a dust bowl as the Americas had in the 1930s and as East Anglia is beginning to have now where they are relying solely on artificial fertilisers. But many modern types of grass are bred for and are reliant, in many respects, on high nitrogen and high output fertiliser treatment. You need both muck and artificial. The modern farmer is being blamed for the nitrates in water but let's put the record straight; 95 per cent of those nitrates are released from root and plant natural breakdown and only about 5 per cent from nitrogenous fertilisers. It started back in wartime when grassland was ploughed up for corn and now, thirty or forty years later, the turf that was turned over and is down in the bottom is still breaking down and is releasing nitrogen into the substrata which eventually gets into the water courses. The arable areas don't help because ploughing breaks down the stubble, and the trash that they plough in every year is breaking down — there's no way you can alter that."

What about the problem of burning straw?

"The big arable farmers don't want to know about straw — they either want to bale it and sell it to the hill farmers who use it for feed and bedding, or burn it. And of course people didn't like the burning — the smoke drifting across motorways, the smut problem in places like Lincoln surrounded by arable areas where the windows were covered and the washing on the line got as black as night — the farmers didn't have a leg to stand on. Now with the setting up of ways to use the straw, wallboards and paper, it could all fit into the Green scene; it's amazing how, when you're pushed into a corner, you find another route. There's even a suggestion that Ethanol could be made from straw; so far it's been uneconomical but with all the extra straw now available there's a chance that a cheap fuel could be produced."

We discussed the effect of "1992" and whether the coming together of the E.E.C. more and more into one unit would mean decrees that certain areas were reserved for certain crops, or animal rearing. Mr Burtt is of the opinion that to a great extent it has happened naturally — "it's a case of horses for courses; we are in fact already specialists in sheep production, we produce the most and best grass. It has always made sense to concentrate on what you are best at and we're unlikely ever to grow olives or limes in Glaisdale unless the Greenhouse Effect sends the weather patterns topsy-turvy.

"Another dubious effect of EEC membership is the new Agrimony terminology; MCA (Monetary Compensatory Allowances), ECU (European Currency Units), Green Pound, Green Lira, etc, etc, all very important but in honesty very few of us fully understand them. Heaven help us if and when we have a common Euro currency and Euro Bank."

But would our nationalistic independent farmers resist being told what to do?

"The milk quotas are an example; we are being persuaded from growing things. You are at liberty to grow and produce what you like, at a certain amount of cost. We've had quotas put on milk production, they've introduced set-aside on cereal growing where they're paid so much an acre not to grow cereals simply because of a surplus of corn. That has had an indifferent reception from farmers although some are taking it up. The interesting thing from a worldwide viewpoint is that the Americans had a 27 per cent setaside programme three or four years ago which put a lot of land out of production and they have now scrapped the scheme completely. One hundred per cent of American cereal land will be back in production in 1989 partly to counter the drought they had in 1988 but also because they want to re-assert themselves on the world market and to beat off the European competition. There's going to be a world war in cereals.

"There have been changes for the sheep farmers, too. They have had a subsidy scheme, a variable premium which topped up the price they received for graded fat lambs at the local auction mart to a guaranteed level. That is changing gradually; it is being reduced by 25 per cent in 1990 and over the next three years will disappear altogether, and what his lambs bring in the market will be all he gets. The money saved is going to be channelled into the Ewe Premium — from a feeder's subsidy to a breeder's subsidy. It's a move into the market place and the farmer has to breed the sheep that the butcher wants, and on that depends the price he will get. It won't make much difference to the high hill sheep man — he's the breeder of the foundation stock. The UK flock has exploded in numbers from 13 million in 1979 to 20 million now, partly because of the profitability of sheep and partly because of the introduction of milk quotas which caused dairy farmers and others to make up their cash shortfall with sheep. The increase in numbers caused havoc in the EEC's subsidy budget and that's what has caused the change, although the EEC is nowhere near self-sufficient in sheep meat and the UK still imports 200,000 tons of New Zealand lamb.

"The poultry farmers had the salmonella crisis and many were forced out of production. The irony is that now we're only producing 75 per cent of the eggs we need and we're importing 25 per cent. There are nineteen tests now being imposed on the UK egg producers and not one test on the continental imports from Holland and France. Why hammer us and not do it to them? You can just as easily get salmonella from a Dutch egg as any other.

"There are two wild cards in assessing the world's requirements, Russia and its satellites, and the Third World. Russia has absorbed millions of tons of grain, beef and butter and one day that is drastically going to decrease. I.C.I., who are the biggest manufacturers of fertilisers in the world, have had a plant and experts in Russia for three or four years. The impact of that must have been beginning to bear fruit before the present upheavals started, but now, in 1990, no-one can say what is going to happen. If parts break away from the Russian Empire, then each of those new states will have to set up their own food chain. They cannot have recourse to the EEC because the food mountains are no longer there but the Americans should be able to help. One of the ironies that has come to light is that Romania was buying butter from the EEC and selling it on to Russia to get cash — they wouldn't keep it for their own population, they couldn't care less about their own people."

He went on to comment that the Americans have underground caverns full of butter just waiting to be released on to the world markets, a much bigger mountain than the E.E.C ever had — and with the advantage that storage is costing them nothing in these deep cool caverns whereas the Europeans had the high cost of refrigeration. "Prior to quotas being introduced in the E.E.C. we had a million tons of butter and a million tons of skimmed milk powder surplus. In 1988 butter was down to 300,000 tons, which is not a bad size of buffer but now it has all disappeared. The milk powder mountain has gone completely. Milk quotas have been very hard on milk producers but have been very effective in reducing surpluses.

"So far as the Third World is concerned there are these horrifying desperate scenes on T.V. of people hungering to death just for the sake of getting food there. People say, 'Why can't we feed the Africans?' and the politicians always come up with good arguments — they can't pay for it, they would forget how to farm for themselves — but when they have nothing there must be some way in spite of bandits, wagons being blown up and the difficulties even when the food gets there. The crux of the matter is that we must be able to supply them on an emergency basis but we must help them to build their own future."

This may all seem remote from the North Yorks Moors farmer trying to make a living; grow less corn, produce less milk, plant more trees, turn your home into a bed and breakfast centre for the holidaymakers who then tramp across your growing crops! Plus the background problem of whether the Ministry of Agriculture or the Ministry of the Environment wins the argument over the future of our green and pleasant acres, whether the control of Environmentally Sensitive Areas, which have been set up in other areas but not yet in the North East, is removed from Agriculture to Environment.

Martin Burtt has strong views: "Some pin-striped civil servant from the Department of the Environment coming to tell a farmer to do this or that will get people's backs up right away. At least the Ministry of Agriculture do know something about farming. We do not want to become National Park keepers. Now, in 1990 there is to be a National Park Review; the Countryside Commission are setting up a body to go round and see if and how the National parks are working and just how liked or disliked they are by the people who live in them. I am part of the NFU team putting together a policy and determining our attitude.

"The National Park department is saying, 'There's a changing attitude in farming — we don't want production for production's sake. Why not let us have the Hill Compensatory Allowance money and let us (the National Park department) pay it out for environment and conservation measures.' That's all very well but farmers are naturally conservationists; the North Yorks Moors are what they are because the farmers are there and have been since time immemorial. The miles of dry stone walls climbing up and down the hillsides would be maintained, the line between heather and grass would remain because it's man-made — and long may it remain so! — but only if it's made financially attractive for the farmers to stay there. Take away the hill subsidies, the linchpin, which have been there since just after the war, then you deny them their income and they're forced off the land."

"Then," said Mr Burtt, "the National Park will revert to a wilderness."